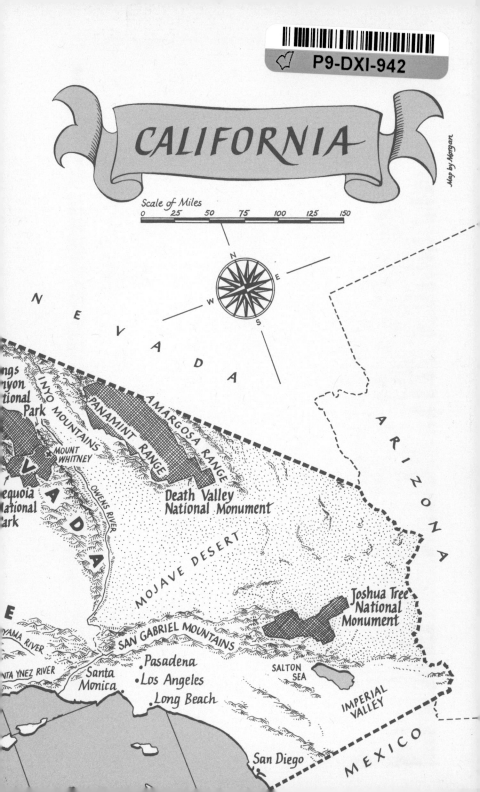

P9-DXI-942

CALIFORNIA

Map by Morgan

Scale of Miles

0   25   50   75   100   125   150

N
W   E
S

NEVADA

INYO MOUNTAINS

PANAMINT RANGE

AMARGOSA RANGE

ARIZONA

ngs
nyon
tional
Park

MOUNT
WHITNEY

NEVADA

OWENS RIVER

equoia
ational
ark

Death Valley
National Monument

MOJAVE DESERT

Joshua Tree
National
Monument

E

YAMA RIVER

SAN GABRIEL MOUNTAINS

SALTON
SEA

TA YNEZ RIVER

Santa
Monica

•Pasadena
•Los Angeles
•Long Beach

IMPERIAL
VALLEY

San Diego

MEXICO

The Destruction of California

By Raymond F. Dasmann

THE LAST HORIZON

THE DESTRUCTION OF CALIFORNIA

53291

RAYMOND F. DASMANN

The Destruction of
CALIFORNIA

THE MACMILLAN COMPANY, NEW YORK
COLLIER–MACMILLAN LIMITED, LONDON

DISCARD

S
932
C 3 D 3

The Author wishes to thank the following for permission to quote passages contained in this book:

University of California Press for material from
The Fur-Bearing Mammals of California, by Grin-
nell, Dixon and Linsdale; and from *Up and Down
California in 1860–1864: The Journal of William
H. Brewer*, edited by Francis P. Farquhar.

Houghton Mifflin Company for material from
John of the Mountains edited by L. M. Wolfe.

Doubleday & Company, Inc. for material from
The Water Seekers by Remi Nadeau.

The California State Library for material from
California, A Guide to the Golden State.

Chappell & Co., Inc. for material from *Camelot*,
copyright © 1960 by Alan Jay Lerner and Frederick
Loewe. Chappell & Co., Inc. publisher and owner of
allied rights throughout the world.

COPYRIGHT © RAYMOND F. DASMANN 1965

All rights reserved. No part of this book may be re-
produced or utilized in any form or by any means,
electronic or mechanical, including photocopying, re-
cording or by any information storage and retrieval
system, without permission in writing from the
Publisher.

First Printing

The Macmillan Company, New York
Collier-Macmillan Canada Ltd., Toronto, Ontario

Library of Congress catalog card number: 65–16936

DESIGNED BY RONALD FARBER

Printed in the United States of America

Contents

Preface

It was with some hesitation that I decided to write this book, and with much more hesitation that I delivered it to the publishers. In this kind of book it is easy to tread on delicate toes, and some of these toes walk on pathways close to mine. I do not intend to annoy my friends and associates, but I am forced to take sides on certain issues. It is much safer to write about a place different from the one in which you live.

In writing this book I have felt at times that I was running a race against the daily news, and must inevitably end by being out of date. Many ideas that seemed new when I wrote them were to be subsequently discussed in the newspapers. In particular I have had the experience of writing parallel to Harold Gilliam of the *San Francisco Chronicle*. On more than one occasion he published material that was almost the same as something I had just finished typing. Since we have had no contact, and I have not yet had the good fortune to meet Mr. Gilliam, it can only be assumed that we are equally alert to the major issues of our time, and read the same books! However, to balance this feeling of being in the vanguard of current thinking, I found that Dr. Joel Hedgpeth had prepared a manuscript for a similar book some twenty years before me. He was kind enough to allow me to look over his manuscript, and although I have not used his material directly, I am indebted to him for ideas.

I wish here to exonerate my relatives, friends, and colleagues in the United States Forest Service, California Department of Fish and Game, Humboldt State College, and other government agencies. They are in no way to be blamed for the material used in this book. The facts that I state are available in published material or are based upon my own observations. The ideas and opinions are my own, although I share them with many others who have also written or spoken about the problems of California. I am writing here as a native of California, concerned with the future of his favorite state, and not from any official position.

I wish to express my appreciation to my wife, who worked with me throughout the preparation of this book and provided the illustrations. I wish also to thank Peter V. Ritner of The Macmillan Company, who suggested that I write a book on the destruction that was taking place in California, and who has helped at every stage of the preparation.

RAYMOND F. DASMANN

Eureka, California
October 19, 1964

ONE

A NOT SO
GOLDEN STATE

California occupies a badly fractured and un-
stable segment of the thin earth crust, along a
coast rising from the sea.   —C. L. CAMP *

I<small>T</small> is easy to write of distant lands visited for a month, or
a year or two, viewed objectively and then left behind. It
is difficult to write of your homeland. There are too many
sides to every mountain; too much tradition lurks by each
stream side; memories cloak the cities. No fact is simply a
fact. It has shades of meaning that defy any clear statement.

In driving across the Bay Bridge early in 1963, I saw
the sign erected to dramatize the population race between
California and New York. There was no question who
would win, on the board if not in reality—the New York
population remained nearly stationary while that of California climbed at the known rate of increase. In just the
few minutes required to drive past, the figures increased
disturbingly. There were those who found joy in this race,

* *Earth Song.* Berkeley, University of California Press, 1952.

and celebrated California's supposed victory. But to some of us there seemed scant cause for rejoicing—just more evidence of the change overtaking the state, a change toward what all the portents showed to be a less desirable condition.

On the far end of the Bay Bridge was San Francisco, her skyline looming against the bank of fog rolling in over the hills from the Pacific. Here was still the queen city, where the sheer geography of location yet defies the efforts of those who care nothing for beauty. The blue of the bay, the glittering stretch of the Golden Gate, the skyline dominated by Diablo and Tamalpais, the array of peninsulas and islands form a setting that would glorify even the most wretched slum. But San Francisco to me is too much a city of memories, haunted by ghosts of the past. It was here that I was born and spent many of my early years. Always I have returned after sojourns in far-off places, and each time I have been again impressed by the magnificence and captivated by the charm of the city. The perspective of time, however, allows me to ask whether the changes that have taken place are for the better or the worse. Try as I may, I cannot feel that things are now better. It is no nostalgia for a past youth that prompts this feeling. I much prefer the life that I live today to anything that I had twenty years earlier. Instead it is a solid objection to physical changes that have taken place, and, more than that, to a spiritual rot that seems to pervade much of the city.

It was more fun in San Francisco, and life was richer when we rode the ferryboats across the bay in 1937, than it is now when we battle the traffic on the bridges. It was more pleasant in 1939, when the Bay Bridge traffic was light and one could enjoy the view, than it will be when there are two Bay bridges, both jammed with autos. The city was more beautiful when the freeways did not cut off the Ferry Building or obstruct the Civic Center. It was more pleasing to ride the cable cars over the city's hills than it is to ride the existing buses, as thousands of tourists prove each year by crowding on the few remaining cables. It was a more exciting trip to go to the zoo on the old streetcar that rocked along the tracks past the sand dunes, than it is to travel by today's vehicles.

San Francisco was a saner, more pleasant city before the great exodus of the middle class toward the suburbs began the blight of its residential sections. It was a better city when men and women, boys and girls, could go anywhere, outside of a few known districts, in daylight or dark, in safety. Better than now, when anyone, regardless of age or sex, risks his welfare or life by straying from the main tourist routes; when its parks and byways are left to the punk and the hoodlum; when the churches must be closed because of the vandal and the pervert.

There is no point in a rebuttal that states the necessity of change, caused by population growth; or that all this is an unfortunate by-product of industrial progress, and a regrettable, temporary concomitant of other desirable gains. Any of these points can be granted. Admittedly, with the present population the old ways would be intolerable. But admit that the city was a brighter, more human, more colorful, more "fun" place to be before this population growth and change, before the industrial gains and their by-product losses. And if this is true, should one not ask whether future change should be tolerated if it is in directions that will make life still less pleasant?

Quite recently I traveled once more by plane to Los Angeles, and was once more stunned by the sheer mass of the place, appearing from the air as one great expanse of similar streets and houses from the mountains to the sea. Los Angeles is still colorful and exciting to those who visit it. Its living conditions, despite the smog, are sufficiently attractive to draw the masses from Iowa and Minnesota, Kansas and Carolina, to escape the blizzard or the summer humidity. But to one who can remember what it once was there seems no cause for cheer—when Santa Monica was a glamorous seacoast place, San Gabriel a colorful mission village nestled against its mountains, Westwood a distinct college community, Hollywood a fascinating world of its own, in spirit, if not geography. Is it better now that the whole mass is blended together and covered with a pall of smoke? Was it really worth while corralling the Colorado, and channeling the waters of northern California, to effect this change? Will the future development make it better or worse?

If you drive up the north coast from Eureka in the early hours, when the mists have not been dispelled by the morning sunlight, you can build up a picture of how things once were, and could be again, in that region. One can ignore the ghosts of the forests of yesterday, and concentrate only on the serried ranks of new trees growing on the logged or burned-over lands. Damage is obscured; the raw edges of the land are blurred by mist. On the left is the blue sea, held flattened by some high-pressure area so that no waves break on the black rock masses that stand above the waters, or against the headlands that drop sheer to thin stretches of sand beach. Timbered peninsulas and curving sand spits enclose the quiet lagoons. A haze covers the still prairies. Mile after mile one goes, and builds the feeling that this is the way a country should be, the way it was intended to look when the forces of creation had finished the job. Crescent City, viewed at sunrise from the ridge where the highway drops down to the plain, seems a sheer jewel of a town, built to fit around its little bay by some group of superior men with a view to how life should be arranged. But the light of midday dispels the grand illusion—the seams show through once more.

In the late evening hours of summer one might visit the grasslands and marshes that remain along the Owens River. There you can see families of sage grouse scatter across the road. Shore birds and a few ducks will fly by. Redwings will be chorusing from the cattails. In the distance the sheer Sierra wall towers against the sunset sky, and behind you the last of the sunlight tops off the high peaks of the White Mountains, challenging the Sierra in height and grandeur. Once more the ugliness and rawness are obscured, and you can see the kind of world that we might still have.

Or just drive up on Twin Peaks and look out over San Francisco on a late October afternoon—you still can; it has not yet been blocked off. With the sun setting behind you, and the city shining in the gold light of autumn, you can see it, despite all that has happened, as the place that it could be.

It is disturbing to a man to find himself out of step with the parade of his times, even if he suspects that others also hear the beat of that different drum. I often wish I could join in the elation of the real-estate developer, building the suburbs for tomorrow's masses, confident that the masses will come and his products will be in demand. Or the secure and comfortable feeling that must envelop the engineer, who with full public support and approval channels yet one more river toward the ever-thirsty southland, or builds one more power station on some previously unvanquished headland. To be in the organized army, even under an idiot commander, brings feelings of comradeship and security lacking to the guerrilla sniping from the rocks. But if the army is marching to the wrong place, to fight the wrong battle, for the wrong cause, what can you do?

It has been said that the problems that face California today, America must meet tomorrow. The waves of the future break first on the rocky California coast; change comes most rapidly. There is truth in this. It misses the point a little, because no place is like any other place, and California is in many ways unique. Yet no one can afford to be unaware of the changes and difficulties that confront California. They are too likely to be the problems of all the civilized world.

California has come a long way since the first man crossed its mountain passes and found it a good place for people. More than four centuries have passed since Cabrillo's ships stood off the bay of San Diego. Almost two hundred years have gone by since Padre Serra and the first settlers came northward. The forty-niners of the nineteenth century, who came seeking gold, have been replaced by those of the twentieth century who came following a dream. California still stands. It is better in many ways than the land that Cabrillo found. No one seriously wants to turn back the clock, to make California once more a way station on the road to the Indies. But one can request, seriously, that in the headlong dash through the last half of the twentieth century we stop for a moment and take stock, that we ascertain our direction, and make sure that the world we are building in the West will be one worth living in.

The lay of the land

Generalizations about any place are dangerous, and more so when the place is diverse and complicated. The popular image of California, presented on the screen, in magazines, and in the news, is true enough, but incomplete. Even the residents have only a partial picture of their home state. Popular California, the section most often seen or portrayed, consists of a small portion of the state: the south coastal area from Santa Barbara to San Diego; the San Francisco–Monterey region; a couple of slices of Sierra, around Tahoe and Yosemite; and a small piece of former desert in the vicinity of Palm Springs. This is typical California, with the famous climate and scenery. But much of the state is not recognizably part of this image. The fog-drenched forests of the north coast are associated with Oregon. The blizzard-whipped sagebrush and juniper of a Modoc winter belong to the Utah-Nevada image. The sun-blasted Mojave is associated with Arizona and New Mexico. The vast agricultural plain of the Central Valley fits the picture of the Middle West. Much of California is un-Californian, and was not even adopted by the Spanish colonists who gave the state its name.

To give a fair description is difficult. No person sees the complete picture. I have been over most of the state by air and highway, have traveled many of its back roads, and have covered remote areas on horseback or on foot. But there is much that I have not seen, except from a distance. California begins with the Pacific, which batters its thousand miles of coastline. Here again the accepted picture is misleading. The sandy beaches, crammed with sun worshipers, occupy only a small part of the coast. Mostly the

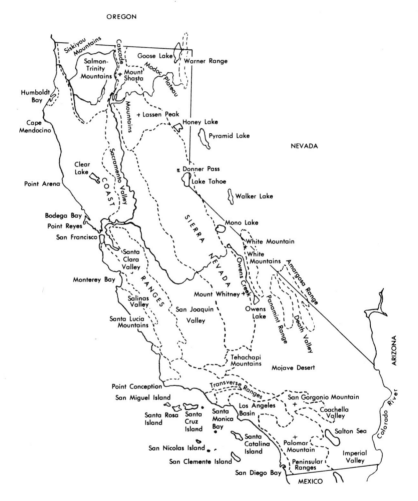

FIG. 1. Where things are—topographic regions.

coast is rocky cliff and headland, battered by the full
strength of waves rolling in from the North Pacific, one
of the most formidable surfs in the world. Each year the
waves claim their toll of victims, fishermen swept from

rocky points, rash boatmen, or abalone hunters who followed the tide for too long.

Inland the state reaches eastward for more than two hundred miles, broken up into most of the climates and vegetation to be found anywhere in the West, along with some that are only in California. From Oregon to Monterey Bay the coastal strip is occupied mostly by coastal forests, similar to those of Oregon and Washington, but differing in that the dominant tree over much of the area is the mighty redwood, a Californian species. These redwood forests have always been described in superlatives, but no account is really exaggerated: they deserve superlatives. Here in the California fog belt they find a last refuge, although in past ages they dominated much of the then humid West, from Alaska southward. Within its California stronghold the redwood seems resistant to most forces of nature. Fire-charred, apparently lifeless snags sprout again; stumps send up new shoots so that ten trees take the place of one; fallen trunks send new trunks growing upward.

The redwood forests are on the coast for only a small part of their range; elsewhere they follow the river valleys inland, and the coast is occupied by other forms of life. In places such as the Kings Range and Santa Lucias, the mountains break steeply down to the sea. Here the coastal vegetation is often brush, a fog-adapted coastal scrub, or coastal sagebrush near the sea, changing with altitude to the summer-scorched chaparral, fields of dense, hard-leaved, in places almost impenetrable, brush. Most of the north coastal region has a climate soaked by heavy winter rains, kept cool through summer by daily fogs, hardly recognizable as "sunny" California.

California's Coast Ranges extend from north of Eureka

south to Santa Barbara County. Farther north and south
they give way to mountains that are coastal, in places, but
not strictly part of the Coast Range complex. The Coast
Ranges are formidable in places, reaching elevations of
over 8,000 feet in the high wilderness of the Yolla Bollys.
Mostly, however, they are low ranges that attain elevations of 3,000 to 4,000 feet, broken everywhere by the
valleys of rivers flowing in a northerly course, cutting
through to the west to enter the Pacific where breaks in
the mountains occur. The Coast Ranges are folded mountains, built mostly from shales and sandstones laid down
long ago when the ocean reached far inland to crash
against the ancestral Sierra.

In the Coast Ranges are covered in their upper reaches by
forests of conifers, pine mostly, but in places fir and
Douglas fir. Most of the lower elevations support the
dense chaparral brush that is typically Californian, even
though most Californians prefer not to claim it. In the
foothills the Coast Ranges and coastal valleys present that
aspect of scenery that is most commonly associated with
the California image, the golden grass and scattered massive oaks, *los robles* of the Spanish, famous from every
mission scene.

In the north the Coast Ranges give way to the wildest
and most tangled mountain complex in the West, the
Klamath Mountains of the geologist, comprising the
Trinitys, the Salmons, the Scotts, and the Siskiyous. Here
craggy peaks, built from ancient rocks, climb nearly 9,000
feet in the air, in wilderness sections that are yet seldom
visited by the tourist. The topography is incredibly complex, and streams flow in all directions to join the Klamath,
the Trinity, or the Sacramento river systems. Here are
some of the state's formally designated wilderness areas,

and other places that may be more wild because they have
not been designated as such to the enlightenment of the
traveler.

Southward the Coast Ranges give way to mountains that
have no name, or none that is generally recognized by
Californians. They are the Peninsular and Transverse
Ranges of the geologist. On detailed maps they become
the Sierra Madre and Santa Ynez, the Topatopas and Tehachapis, the Santa Anas, Santa Rosas, San Gabriels, and
San Jacintos. They were the mountains best known to the
Spanish, but the Spanish seemed to travel in them little.
They climb to over 11,500 feet on San Gorgonio mountain,
transecting every life zone from the hot desert to the cold
alpine. In the Los Padres National Forest they break
against one of the most densely populated sections of the
state, and yet remain remote and wild, the last breeding
grounds of the condor. In the Angeles National Forest
they look down upon the millions of city dwellers, yet support the wild and wary bighorn sheep. In the Tehachapis
they form the barrier that separates the rest of California
from the world of Southern California. The phrase "south
of the Tehachapis" indicates to the Northern Californian
that the region in question is not within any worthwhile
portion of the world.

In Northern California, as you travel inland through
the wild Klamath Mountains, you see from every ridge
top a landmark that could well symbolize California,
Mount Shasta. This is a sheer jewel of a mountain—a great
volcanic cone that reaches up more than 14,000 feet in the
air. Not many centuries ago it covered California with
plumes of smoke and ash and sent lava cascading down
its sides. Today it is rated as extinct, meaning that for a
long time it has been quiescent. Its upper slopes bear gla-

Crescent City

Alturas

Arcata
Eureka
Redding

Susanville

Fort Bragg
Willits

Reno
Carson City

· Marysville

Santa Rosa ·
Sonoma ·
Napa ·
Vallejo
□ Sacramento

San Francisco
Oakland
□ Stockton

San Jose

Bishop·
Big Pine ·

Santa Cruz

Monterey
Carmel
Salinas
Fresno
· Lone Pine

Las Vegas □
Hoover Dam

Morro Bay
San Luis
Obispo
□ Bakersfield

Santa Barbara
Ventura
Pomona
San Bernardino
Parker Dam·

Los Angeles
Santa Ana
· Palm Springs
· Coachella

Oceanside

San Diego
Imperial
Yuma

FIG. 2. Where things are—some towns and cities

ciers through the summertime. In winter the whole mountain is covered with a blanket of snow. Shasta is part of a different mountain system, the Cascade Range, that runs through Oregon and Washington. In California the Cascades extend to the southeast of Shasta, to terminate in the 10,000-foot peak of Mount Lassen, the only volcano in the continental United States rated as active. Lassen, after being considered extinct, surprised the world in 1914 by blasting a new crater on its once peaceful summit and sending great clouds of ash thousands of feet skyward. Eruptions continued for several years, and new lava flows smashed and covered forests on its slopes. Lassen is once more quiescent, but no one dares call it extinct. South from Lassen, the turbulent Cascades give way to the solid granite massif of the Sierra Nevada.

Related to the Cascade Range is the Modoc Plateau, a great area of lava field that covers the northeastern corner of the state. Here the lava is not from volcanoes, but poured out of great fissures that opened in the earth many millions of years ago. On cooling, the surface of the lava fragmented into boulders of basalt that today, even after a long period of weathering, make travel through this country difficult. The Modoc region provided a last stronghold for warlike California Indians. Here, in the 1870's, sixty warriors of the Modoc tribe held 1,200 United States soldiers at bay for a period of five months. Had the Indians won the war, this episode would rival our tale of the Alamo in song and legend. Anyone who has seen the lava fortresses where the Indians held out can understand how the feat was accomplished.

The heart of California is the Central Valley, including that of the Sacramento River on the north and of the San Joaquin on the south. This is the land that once cheered the pioneers who had struggled westward over the Sierra passes. Only when they saw the valley stretched before them did they feel that they had reached a goal. More flat than most of the Middle West, the Central Valley extends nearly four hundred miles from the Klamaths to the Tehachapis, and sixty miles east and west from the coastal mountains to the Sierra foothills. To the Spanish the San Joaquin was the great "Tule Valley," or "Valley of the Lakes," a name that is not applicable at all today. The Sacramento was noted as a great sea of grass, dotted with giant white oaks. Once the Central Valley received all the waters that drain from the Sierra westward, or eastward from the Klamaths and the Coast Ranges. Now most of the historic tributaries of the Sacramento and San Joaquin have been dammed, and their waters channeled away. Where great herds of wild game and cattle roamed, farm lands now produce much of the food consumed in California.

Dominating the scene in Central California is the Sierra Nevada, the Snowy Range, which reaches for nearly four hundred miles from Lassen County in the north to the Tehachapis. This great granitic mountain block is the most formidable mountain barrier in the continental United States, and still proves an obstacle to travel eastward from California. Since almost unbelievable amounts of snow sometimes cover its mountain passes, even the superhighways of today can be closed in wintertime. In the past, when men struggled up its slopes with their oxcarts, the Sierra proved the final insurmountable barrier for many an unfortunate pioneer. Viewed from the California side, the Sierra is deceptive, for it slopes gently eastward for as much as sixty miles, and only slowly gains altitude. But viewed from the east, its 14,000-foot peaks form, in places, a sheer, impassable mountain wall. From Diamond Mountain in the north, the Sierra crest seldom drops below 7,000 feet, and at Mount Whitney in the south it attains 14,496 feet, the highest point south of Canada. Along with supporting great stands of timber, and providing people with a recreational wonderland, the Sierra serves its function as a gatherer of the water upon which California depends. Every air mass that moves eastward from the Pacific is forced to give up its rain before leaving the state, so that eastward from the Sierra the land is left desolate and dry. The desert lands of California occupy more space than any other single region of the state. Everything to the east of the Southern California mountains is desert. Here the rainfall averages only a few inches; meaning that sometimes there is none and in other years as much as ten inches. Being desert, however, does not mean that the land is completely barren. Apart from the salt flats, or alkali plains, most of the desert supports a sparse cover of vegetation—creosote bush or cactus. Following the occasional rain, the desert may bloom with a colorful mass of flowers. The deserts achieve their most formidable aspect in Death Valley, where a great block of land between the Panamints and Amargosa Mountains has sunk down to 280 feet below sea level. Here at Greenland Ranch, where the rainfall averages less than one and a half inches per year, a shade temperature of 134 degrees was once recorded by the weather station. Where the soils were suitable, and water has been made available, as in the Imperial Valley, the desert has been changed into a subtropical agricultural paradise.

North of the true desert, arid conditions occur to the east of the Sierra in the Great Basin region of California. This country with its sagebrush and alkali flats is essentially similar to Nevada, and, like that state, includes isolated mountain ranges. In California these include the beautiful 9,000-foot Warner Mountains of the far northeast, and directly across the Owens Valley from the Sierra, the White Mountains that reach more than 14,000 feet in elevation.

In considering the topography of California, it is well to remember that the state forms a part of what Griffith Taylor has called the "ring of fire" surrounding the Pacific Basin. This is a ring of volcanic mountains and major earthquake faults that extends from New Zealand northward to Japan, across to Alaska, and down the Pacific Coast of the Americas. The entire ring is a scene of disturbance and instability. Major earthquakes occur when slips occur along the fault lines; volcanic activity flares and dies down, only to flare again. Californians forget their past, and prefer not to dwell on the subject of earthquakes, but the state is plagued with them. A glance at any relief map will show their center of origin in the great San Andreas Fault. From Point Arena across the waters to Bodega Head and Tomales Bay, then to Bolinas Bay and into the ocean off San Francisco, the fault line is visible. South of San Francisco is a chain of fault-line lakes that shows its path through the Santa Cruz Mountains. Still southward one can follow it by the mountain folds to where it crosses the Tehachapis. It follows the desert side of the Southern Californian mountains through the Imperial Valley to disappear finally in the Gulf of California. Joining the main fault are branch lines. Most significant is the one that extends up the east side of the Sierra.

Earthquakes have shaken California over the centuries. The sheer face of the Sierra was formed by the sinking of blocks of ground along the fault line through the Owens Valley–Mono Lake region. The process has not halted. In 1872 the village of Lone Pine was destroyed in a major quake that caused one block of ground to drop as much as twenty feet, leaving a sheer scarp. The disastrous earthquake that destroyed San Francisco in 1906 also produced strange effects on the countryside. At Olema in Marin

County a formerly straight road, crossing the San Andreas Fault, was offset twenty-one feet as the land on the west side of the fault moved north in relation to that on the east side. Elsewhere in Marin and Sonoma counties, the earth opened up and swallowed a cow, and a large redwood tree, growing on the fault, was neatly split in two.

California and Nevada have had an average of five thousand earthquakes a year since the first one greeted Padre Serra in 1769. Most of these are noticeable only to a seismograph, but during the past thirty years major damage has been done by earthquakes in Long Beach, Bakersfield, and Eureka. None of these have been as severe as the quake that hit the Yellowstone Region in 1959, the one that devastated Chile in 1960, or the Alaska quake of 1964. But it is a certainty that earthquakes of major intensity will hit California again. Builders who fail to consider this gamble with human lives.

It is also certain that California's volcanoes have not retired from action. John Muir recalls a tradition of the Pit River Indians of a "Fearful time of darkness, when the sky was black with ashes and smoke that threatened every living thing with death." * Such times will occur again. In any planning for the future development of a state known for its earthquake faults, its steaming geysers, and its volcanic cones, the geological facts of life should be considered.

Far more than earthquakes or volcanoes, the climate of California has been publicized throughout the world. The thought of orange groves by the blue sea, or roses and surf bathing on New Year's Day, has sent many a Midwesterner to packing his bags. But California's climates, like all else about the state, are diverse. Three major cli-

* *The Mountains of California* (New York, Century, 1913).

matic regions occur, from the subtropical one of Southern California, through warm temperature to cool temperate in the northern part of the state. The basic pattern through much of the state is the same. Winter is the wet season and over most of the state is cool or cold. Summer is almost everywhere dry, between April and October. Plant growth starts after the fall rains, and by midwinter the hills are green with grass. Spring is the main growing season, but by May most hills are sere and growth has ceased. But this generalization does not everywhere hold. Winter storms and cold are as severe in the California mountains as in Minnesota. Temperatures as low as 56 degrees below zero have been recorded on Mount Lassen. Snowfall as high as 844 inches in a single winter was recorded at Tamarack in the central Sierra—more than 70 feet of snow. At the other extreme the annual rainfall and temperature in parts of the Mojave are as extreme as those of any tropical desert. The Californian who is finicky about climates has a wide choice. He can find places where he will seldom see the sun, and places where rain seldom falls. He can settle where there are no marked seasonal changes, or in places where the seasons are as clearly marked as anywhere in the country. Most likely, wherever he settles, he will find some reason to complain about the weather.

The influence of people

In much of California today it is not the physical geography or the climate, but the influence of man that is most impressive. Furthermore it is not the *status quo,* the existing effects that man has had on the land, but the obvious rate of change that commands attention. In every mountain area and every valley this change is going on, so that one can hardly count on the stability of any single feature other than the broadest and most dominating geographic aspects of the country. Already we have filled the San Francisco Bay basin with housing, industry, airfields, and highways, from the tops of the hills to the edge of the water. The same thing has happened to Los Angeles. In the Central Valley, from the head of the sloughs leading to San Francisco Bay as far east as the Sierra foothills, one housing tract replaces another in a formless mass of suburbs that have been aptly termed "slurbs." If it could end at this it would be bad enough, but reparable. Instead, the process goes on. Housing and industry spread ever farther, engulfing farm and forest, marsh and pasture with no end in sight except the dismal one of a gigantic, disorganized megalopolis, filling much of the state and depending for its food on distant lands.

At present California is laced with a network of highways that alone occupy a significant percentage of its total land area. Some are huge freeways with eight or more lanes of traffic. Each day the freeway system spreads, over more land. No one who has driven the old two-lane stretches, fighting the mass of produce trucks, tourists with trailers, logging rigs, and other highway monsters can do other than demand more freeways. Yet the freeways themselves become so hopelessly crowded that travel anywhere becomes painful. One wonders where the process will halt, at what point further expansion will become absurd, and motorcar travel must be abandoned in favor of some less space-consuming method of transport.

The most disturbing change that is taking place in California involves the state's water resources. The California state water plan includes the most massive engineering undertaking attempted anywhere. When completed, every river of consequence in California will have been dammed, once or many times. Waters that once flowed down the Eel or Klamath into the Pacific will be pumped back over mountains, through tunnels into the Central Valley. All of the northern part of the state, where rainfall is high, will send water to the dry lands of the south. Here the availability of water will encourage further growth of population and industry that will in turn create fresh demand for water, until every drop that can be captured anywhere will be used and reused. And then what happens? Are we planning for this day? Or do we expect some Armaggedon to intervene before we must reach this final decision?

Get involved with any sort of planning in California, and inevitably a mass of conflict and contradiction will emerge. Every acre of land is being used in somebody's scheme for often conflicting purposes. No one seems willing to look far enough ahead. One feels a lack of value judgments and an unwillingness to face the question "Do we really want the kind of a world that we appear committed to build?"

I cling to the hope that people are rational beings, or can become such, and that when faced with obvious alternatives they will choose the one most favorable to their survival. That they are not at the mercy of blind forces beyond human control. It is a belief that we can create and maintain a world fit for free men to dwell in—that we are not bound inevitably toward an anthill existence, fit only for creatures that are less than men.

What is the threat to California, and from whom does it stem? The threat comes essentially from all who do not know what California was, cannot see what it is, cannot dream of what it could be. The enemies are those who have looked so long into the blast furnaces of civilization that they can no longer appreciate a sunset—those to whom growth is progress and progress is good, regardless of its direction—those to whom money is the single standard against which all else must be measured. California has been hacked and battered by the forces of ignorance and greed, and is today being forced in a direction that few would want to travel if they could see what lay ahead.

So it is that in California one sees not only the consequence of unplanned, careless, or deliberately destructive past activity; one also gets the feeling that the worst is yet to come. There are times when the change without apparent direction, and the growth without control, give the appearance of socially acceptable madness, of a human population irruption that may well end tragically both for the people and for the land.

TWO

IT BELONGED TO
THE INDIANS

Know that on the right hand of the Indies
there is an island called California, very near to
the Terrestrial Paradise. . . .
            —GARCÍA ORDÓÑEZ DE MONTALVO *

THE land was shaped by earthquakes and the outpourings of volcanoes, by the warping, twisting, and folding of the earth's crust. It was carved by the rivers, and its harsh outlines were smoothed by their loads of silt and sand dropped on outwash plains or in the beds of ancient seas. It was polished by glaciers that formed in its mountains and flowed down the canyons during the tens of thousands of glacial years. It was baked by the sun and leached by rain over the millennia. It grew a covering of plants, in places dense and luxuriant, hiding the land; elsewhere managing only a scant foothold on harsh rock or shifting sand. Animals in thousands of species and millions of individuals came to occupy it. Then, late in the scheme of things, one species that was to dominate and remake the entire land arrived on the scene.

* Las Sergas de Esplandián. Toledo. 1510.

At some point in the dim vistas of past time men first came to California. Most likely they drifted in across the plains and between the mountain ranges of what is now the Mojave Desert, driven westward into unknown lands by some social turmoil or economic scarcity in their former homeland. They settled in no one place and built no permanent homes, for they were hunters whose lives depended on going where game was most abundant. Perhaps they belonged to the group called Folsom men, named from the town in New Mexico near where their artifacts were first found. If so, they were skilled hunters indeed, armed with spear throwers with which they could bring down the largest mammoth or the giant bisons of those days. Throughout the West have been found the stone spearheads, Folsom points, that designate their culture. But men may have come still earlier in time, before the Folsom way of life was developed. Their time of arrival and the extent of their occupancy of the land of California remain a mystery.

It is fairly certain that man first reached America by traveling overland from Asia by way of the Bering Strait. This was accomplished, most likely, during the last great Ice Age, the Wisconsin Glacial Age, at a time when ice sheets covered much of the Northern Hemisphere and sea levels were low enough to create a land bridge between the continents. The Wisconsin Age was marked by four periods during which the ice advanced, known as substages, and four intervals during which glacial retreat took place. The last ice advance of Wisconsin times, the Mankato Substage, reached its peak in the years around 9,000 B.C. By then man was established throughout the Americas, all the way from Alaska to Tierra del Fuego. Some evidence suggests that man was widely distributed in the New World

30,000 years ago. On Santa Rosa Island, off the coast of Southern California, the roasted bones of a dwarf race of the extinct mammoth have been found associated with what is thought to be an early campfire. These remains are more than 29,000 years old. In Mexico have been found carvings on the bones of mammoths and mastodons that are thought to date back even further, perhaps beyond the Wisconsin Ice Age into the long preceding Sangamon Interglacial Period. Since it is a long, slow journey on foot from the Bering Strait to Mexico for people who did not know where they were going or why they were going there, we can only assume that the first men reached America well before 30,000 B.C. The experts on anthropology have been reluctant to assign any great antiquity to man in the New World, but each new discovery has shifted their time-table farther back into the past.

The lands of California when man first arrived were far different than today. Thus, during glacial times the Channel Islands were connected to the mainland coast, and the Gulf of California extended up into the present Salton Sea. The volcanic Cascade Range went through cycles of great activity, reaching a shattering crescendo when Mount Mazama in southern Oregon blew its top, collapsed into itself, and formed the setting for Crater Lake. In the process it covered a great area with ash and debris and buried the belongings of a group of people who were already residing in eastern Oregon at that time—4500 B.C. The California peaks of Shasta and Lassen must have participated in these waves of activity, and new layers of lava must have been added to the Modoc Plateau. During the major ice advances, glaciers blanketed much of the Sierra Nevada, south of what is now Donner Pass, and in places formed continuous ice mantles. On the east side of the mountains glaciers dropped icebergs into a vastly larger Mono Lake, and helped to carve and form Lake Tahoe. On the west side the glaciers moved down the long river canyons and carved one of them into the scenic masterpiece of the Yosemite. Over the now dry parts of the state, pluvial conditions prevailed while the glaciers were present. Pyramid Lake in Nevada was joined with such now alkaline lakes as Honey Lake in California to form the great glacial Lake Lahontan. All of the now dry lakes of the Mojave region were then filled. In the Inyo country, Owens Lake overflowed into Searles and China lakes, now dust beds. These in turn continued into Death Valley and Panamint Valley to form lakes that were in places more than 900 feet deep. The Central Valley at times must have been a morass of marsh and swamp.

Following the last, Mankato, ice advance, when man was established on the California scene, the climate began to change from cool and humid to warm and dry, toward a climatic period known as the "climatic optimum" in northern Europe, because of the mild climates it brought to this region, but better regarded as the "thermal maximum" because of the excess of heat and drought it brought to the American West. Beginning around 6,000 B.C., the thermal maximum period endured, probably with some alleviating intervals, for several thousands of years, and brought an extension of deserts and aridity that has not been paralleled since. Lakes that now hold water were then dry. Glaciers vanished from even the now ice-capped peaks of the highest mountains.

The sequence of these major climatic changes has been traced through the occurrence of animal and plant remains discovered in the La Brea tar pits in present-day Los Angeles. These asphalt pools trapped all animals that ventured into them, and preserved their remains for our examination. The early La Brea period, marked by the oldest fossils, was one when the climate was hot and dry and the plant life similar to that now found several hundred miles to the south. This was most probably an interglacial period. Following this the climate became warm and humid, and the vegetation that developed was sufficiently lush to support such swamp-dwelling creatures as the tapir, now found in southern Mexico. Perhaps at this time the oceans were warmed sufficiently to contribute the excess amounts of precipitation needed to build up the glaciers on the mountains. Following the warm-humid period a cool stage occurred that may well have coincided with the Mankato ice advance. The climate was still moist, and the area supported live-oak and pine forests. Great numbers of mastodons and other large mammals were trapped in the tar at this time. Next, coinciding with the thermal maximum of aridity, desert plants were found in the area, and with them such desert animals as the peccary, now found no closer than southern Arizona. Finally the cooler and more moist climate of the present day appeared, and only modern plants and animals are found trapped in the tar.

During these climatic and geographic changes the plant species found in California did not differ from what they are today, but the total character of all of the plants in an area, the vegetation, did change back and forth as forests moved southward or down mountain slopes when the climate was cool and moist, or as deserts extended northward or moved up mountainsides during the hot, dry periods. The surprising feature in the changing pattern of life is that the plants that now support only a small variety of large mammals at that time provided food for an impressive array of animal life that today can barely be matched on the plains of Africa. Great numbers of mammoths and mastodons, native American horses and llama-like camels, giant and small ground sloths and bisons, larger and more voracious carnivores, such as outsized wolves and saber-toothed cats, wandered over the California plains in association with the species that still survive today. Coyotes, which now slay an occasional sheep, then scavenged on mastodons.

The herds of game were the most important natural resource in California on which all human life depended during glacial and postglacial times. The hunting men built their campsites around the edges of now dry desert lakes and left their spearpoints mixed in with the bones of the game. These hunting peoples have left their traces all over the arid West, in caves, rock shelters, or alluvial deposits. We find their remains associated with giant ground sloths at Gypsum Cave near Las Vegas, dating from 6500 years before Christ. In the San Joaquin Valley the remains of these early men are found mixed with the bones of extinct camels. However, by 6,000 b.c. the first of the great changes in human life in California was beginning. During the next thousand years, and most likely during a relatively short period of that millennium, men were to hunt the last of the big game and then, with the animals gone, were to be forced to find a new way of living.

It is not possible to know why the great mammals of the late Ice Age vanished from the scene, leaving only a relatively small number of species in their place. The disappearance of mammoth, horse, camel, sloth, and perhaps mastodon, however, appear to be associated with the hot and dry period that hit the western part of North America. Perhaps the dryness spread so widely as to restrict the area suitable for the support of the game. Perhaps in those areas where enough rain fell to produce forage, too many animals were forced to concentrate. Under such circumstances the destruction of forage by overgrazing could have caused massive losses of game, just as a similar combination of drought and grazing pressure was to decimate California's livestock during historical times. It may be that man was a factor in giving the final push into extinction to the remaining pockets of game through concentration of hunting efforts. Whatever the cause, the animals disappeared, and with the animals the old hunting cultures were also doomed. If we could find the cause it would be valuable, since we might better predict the course of the future. There is no guarantee that the great drought will not return to California. Climatic changes usually do not move in a one-way direction. Past conditions usually recur.

I do not know whether the peoples who once lived by hunting the big game of postglacial California died out and were replaced by later comers, or whether they were able to adapt to a different way of life. Elsewhere in America, however, a major change in culture was taking place. People continued to hunt the smaller game that was left, but hunting became a secondary pursuit, and the major effort was directed toward the collection of plant foods. Men became experts at seeking out edible plants and watching over the supply. Eventually they learned to propagate them. Coincident with the disappearance of the game herds, the agricultural way of life had its beginnings in the Americas. In California, however, this new way of living did not emerge. The people who replaced the early hunters came equipped with bow and arrow in place of the spear thrower. More importantly, they came equipped with the ability to make use of the great variety of wild plants that the region then possessed. Perhaps because the wild plants were adequate for staple food, and because there was enough small game and fish to satisfy their needs, the Indians of California did not turn to agriculture. Indeed, they failed to take up any of the more strenuous pursuits that Europeans later were to consider praiseworthy. Encouraged by adequate food and a mild climate, the early Californians tended not to advance culturally but to slip backward. Only invasions from the east and north brought the kind of change that we have learned to call progress. Perhaps there is something about the atmosphere of the state that makes its native sons prefer the older ways and the *status quo*.

It is tempting to try to build up a picture that establishes California as a haven for peculiar ways of life and odd groups of people that elsewhere tend to perish in the general march of progress. There would be some truth in this, but the picture would be too comforting for some of us, and is hardly borne out by the events of the middle decades of the twentieth century. Nevertheless, during the long, quiet centuries before the European appeared on the scene California was a haven for a great variety of Indians, most of whom would have to be called "backward" by the standards of Arizona, Mexico, or the eastern United States. They had none of the diligence of the Iroquois, none of the dash and color of the Blackfeet or Sioux, none of the civilized "virtues" of the Pueblo, Aztec, or Mayan. For centuries on end they ground acorns, went clamming, caught fish, or lazed in the sun, and the only lasting monuments that they built were the garbage heaps that we know as shell mounds. Usually they did not even bother to spend time on that uniquely civilized practice, warfare, but lived in peace with their neighbors. For this indolence they were to be despised and condemned by later comers.

Although in most of the books that describe the Indians of North America the Californians are considered as a group and dismissed in a brief chapter, they were actually a highly diversified array of peoples speaking many languages and coming from many origins. Without agriculture they managed to support themselves in remarkably high numbers. In Indian times as well as today California led the rest of the United States in population, and the major centers of concentration were in the same general areas as where they are now located. It is estimated that one-tenth of the total Indian population of the United States, before white settlement, some 130,000 people, lived in California.

The California Indians belonging to the language group known as the Hokan were probably the first to inhabit the state. They developed the most unique and distinctive aboriginal culture of the California region in the area occupied by the Pomo Indians along the coast north of San Francisco Bay. At one time they ranged over the entire state. To the Yahi tribe of this Hokan group belonged the famous Ishi, whose story has been told recently in the book by Theodora Kroeber, *Ishi in Two Worlds*. Long after people had forgotten the existence of wild Indians, in 1910, Ishi came out of the rugged canyon of Deer Creek near Red Bluff, to become a captive of the civilized world that had grown up around him. For forty years, he and his few surviving relatives had lived as refugees from the white people who had virtually exterminated their tribe in the late 1860's and early 1870's. Only the steep lava cliffs, caves, and dense brush protected them from discovery and

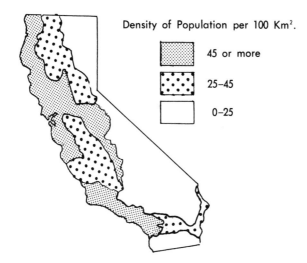

Density of Population per 100 Km².

45 or more

25–45

0–25

FIG. 3. California supported more Indians than any other region of comparable size in the United States. Many of the old centers of Indian population are still centers where people concentrate today. The map shows the density of Indians before European settlement. *Source: Heizer and Whipple,* California Indians, *1951*

permitted them to carry on in their old ways. Ishi was, however, to be adopted by the University of California museum of anthropology, and lived to teach the university anthropologists much about the culture of the primitive California Indians.

The Hokan-speaking Indians were displaced at some early time in California history by an invasion of the Penutian-speaking tribes, represented by the Indians of the Yosemite region, the much-studied Miwoks. These in turn were to be displaced by a later invasion from east of the Sierra by the Shoshonean Indians, of which the Utes and Paiutes are best known. These took over the northeastern and much of the southern part of the state. Another group of invaders followed the salmon fisheries down the north-coast rivers. These belonged to the widespread Atha-bascan-Algonkian group, widely represented through Canada and Alaska. The Hupas and Yuroks are representative tribes who still fish for salmon in the rivers of the California northwest. Thus, through various successive waves of invasion from the east and north the patchwork of diverse tribes that occupied California when the Europeans first arrived was to be formed.

Most of the California Indians learned one trick that was to be characteristic of their culture, an ability to deal with, and a consequent dependence on, acorns produced by the widespread, abundant oak trees of the country. Most of the California tribes could grind acorns into meal and leach this to extract the bitter tannin and make it palatable. Acorns rather than corn or buffalo meat were the staff of life in Indian California. These were supplemented by a wide variety of edible plants and by animal foods ranging from grasshoppers and sea mussels to elk and antelope.

The second chapter of man's story in California, in which a quiet balance existed between man and wild nature, was brought to an end by the arrival of people from the world of ships and cities. The first sail to appear off the California coast brought a portent that the old way of life was ending. We do not know who was in the first ship to arrive from across the sea. Some think they were Ming-dynasty seafarers in a Chinese junk. Most likely the ship had trimmer lines, and flew the colors of Spain.

While the Indians of California continued undisturbed in their old ways, their brethren elsewhere in the Americas were being faced with the reality of an alien, powerful, and basically hostile culture. The Vikings had come and gone in the East, making little impression. Columbus came and sailed away again, bringing little immediate change. But Columbus returned, and others followed in a growing stream. The Indians who had followed the paths of progress in Mexico and Peru were robbed and slaughtered. Those who followed the farming way of life in the agricultural East saw their lands taken from them. Those who followed the buffalo on the Great Plains saw trouble when a small armed band of conquistadors came northward from the conquered lands of Mexico. But in California, nothing changed.

Out on the bleak Channel Islands where the sound of wind and breaking surf now muffles the noise of guided missiles heading seaward from Point Mugu is the grave of a man known as the discoverer of California, Juan Rodríguez Cabrillo. To the surprise and consternation of the Indians, he appeared in the year 1542 with his two small ships after a voyage of three months' duration. He landed at a safe harbor to be known as San Diego. The Indians of the Channel Islands, themselves seafarers in their plank canoes, were confronted by Cabrillo and his followers as he explored along the coast. But having escaped the hazards of the sea, Cabrillo was to die in California from injuries received when he fell from a rock. He was buried on the island of San Miguel on January 3, 1543, the first of the visitors from an alien world to remain permanently in California. His arrival was an indication of the changes that were to come, but generations of Indians were to live and die, and his visit was to become a dim legend, before those changes were to take place.

Cabrillo's ships, under the command of Bartolomé Ferrelo, returned to Mexico to report to the Viceroy who governed in the name of the King of Spain. They brought no gold, nor did they report a paradise to be found in the lands to the north. They could tell only of a bleak coast and primitive savages. Spain and Mexico had other concerns, and California was forgotten for a time. Indeed, California might have been completely neglected were it not that Elizabeth of England had seen fit to send out a little British ship, the *Golden Hind,* under the command of Sir Francis Drake, into the seas of the Western world. Drake sighted land at Point Reyes in 1579, overawed the Indians, and anchored in a place to be called Drake's Bay. Here he claimed the entire land in the name of his sovereign. Unwillingly, and only to protect her Mexican hegemony, Spain was brought into the picture once more. By this time, however, the lands to the north had acquired some potential practical value in the eyes of the Viceroy in Mexico. Spanish galleons had begun to sail across the Pacific, finally to tap the wealth of the Indies. Laden with cargo from the Philippines, they followed the winds north and east from Manila, across the ocean, to sight land on the California coast. Thus, to find safe anchorage for these Manila galleons, and to establish more firmly the Spanish claim to the land, new expeditions were sent forth from Mexico. In 1584 Francisco Gali sailed north from Acapulco to explore the California coast. He was followed in 1595 by Sebastián Cermeno, who on a return voyage from Manila first sighted the Bay of Monterey. A major expedition came in 1602 when Sebastián Vizcaíno went forth, rediscovered San Diego Bay, and finally left such a misleading description of Monterey Bay as to make it almost unrecognizable. But other than relocating potential harbors and creating some stir among the natives, these expeditions had little effect. For more than two centuries after its discovery, while the British colonies on the eastern sea-board pressed toward independence, and while Spain and Portugal came to share the ownership of all Latin America, California remained undisturbed.

The old history of California takes on a modern tone with the entrance of the Russians on the stage. The practice of doing the right thing, at long last, only to keep the Russians from doing it first is not new. Thus, when Vitus Bering, pursuing the fur trade, flew the flag of the Czar from Alaska and penetrated on down the Pacific Coast the Spanish finally became alarmed. It was a slow-burning alarm that created no action for several decades. But finally, in 1769, a colonizing expedition was sent forth. California, for better or worse, was to be added to the civilized world.

A little band of Spanish and Indians under the leadership of Don Gaspar de Portolá and the spiritual guidance of Padre Junípero Serra pushed north from Baja California to reach San Diego and begin the establishment of the first California mission in 1769. Shortly thereafter Portolá went north to find Monterey Bay; but, misled by the glowing description left by Vizcaíno, he failed to recognize its rather minor harbor, and stumbled on northward to discover San Francisco Bay instead. Soon afterward an expedition went out from the Spanish settlements in Arizona, under the leadership of Juan Bautista de Anza. This crossed the forbidding deserts and reached San Diego. Thereafter an increasing number of expeditions moved north from Mexico by land or sea, bringing colonists, livestock, and supplies. Settlements spread up the coast. California became firmly attached to the Spanish empire. The Spanish way of life came to displace the old Indian culture in part, and bring to these older inhabitants of the country the mixed blessings of Christian civilization. An imprint of Spain and of Mexico was to be placed on California that was not to be erased. Despite the many changes that were to come, the Spanish influence was to remain.

Considering the expansionist habits of most groups of settlers in the New World it is interesting that the Spanish Californians restricted their area of settlement to only a small part of the California territory. Perhaps the necessity for remaining close to the ports that formed a line of communication with the homeland seemed of most importance, but perhaps also they were attracted by the climate and landscape of south-coastal California and found them reminiscent of the climate and lands of Spain. Whatever the cause, they found little to attract them in the Central Valley, which they explored, or the Sierra Nevada, which they barely touched. The dense forests and hostile Indians of the north coast repelled them further. Their settlements were restricted mostly to the warm and pleasant coastal valleys near the sea.

Like the Indians before them, the Spanish settlers seemed to succumb to the spell of their new homeland. Far from being culturally progressive, they seemed to lapse quickly into indolent ways of minimum work and maximum rest and play. Supported by the luxuriant range lands that invited their cattle and sheep to multiply and prosper, and the fertile coastal soils that grew their grains, vines, and orchards, they found little need for strenuous effort. Indians were present in sufficient numbers to do much of the heavy work, however unwillingly. For the eighty years that it was to endure, while the new United States to the east and north bustled with activity and burst their boundaries in expansion, the Californians were busy establishing a pattern for leisurely living that, like the

Cabrillo, 1542

Area of Russian Settlement
Fort Ross
Bodega
+ Sonoma
Drake, 1579 ×
San Francisco
Dolores
San Rafael
+ San Jose
+ Santa Clara
Santa Cruz
Vizcaino, 1602 ×
+ San Juan Bautista
Monterey
Carmel
+ Soledad
+ San Antonio
+ San Miguel
+ San Luis Obispo
Santa Ynez
Purisima +
+ Santa Barbara
+ San Fernando
Buenaventura +
+ San Gabriel
Cabrillo, 1543
Los Angeles Pueblo
+ San Juan Capistrano
+ San Luis Rey
+ San Diego

FIG. 4. The Spanish settled those areas of California with the most congenial environment. The great valley, high mountains, and forested lands were avoided. This map shows the missions and presidios of Spanish California.

names they left upon the land, was to become a permanent part of the California tradition.

One can only speculate on what California would be like had it remained part of Latin America. Today, simply by crossing the border into Baja California one enters a Mexican world that has the same soils, the same climate, but an entirely different cultural aspect from the land on the northern side. Yet with its splendid harbors and fertile agricultural soils, it seems hardly likely that California could have remained in the same condition as northern Mexico. More likely a parallel could be found in Chile, where the same climate, good harbors, and rich agricultural soils are to be found. But a Chile of the north was not to be. Instead, gold, the yellow metal that the Spanish had sought so eagerly throughout Latin America, was to bring an end to the Latin rule in this northerly outpost of Spanish culture.

THREE

WHERE ANTELOPE GLIMMERED THROUGH THE DANCING HEAT

We need all the dogs, all the cats, and all the
birds, and all the elephants we can find. . . .
We need all the friendship we can find around
us.   —ROMAIN GARY *

I wish I could awaken through some magic of the written
word a desire for wildlife conservation among those who
care not about it. Some books that I read as a child accomplished this for me. Those of Ernest Thompson Seton and
Jack London come to mind. But I was already inclined in
that direction ever since I was first exposed to wild country
at the age of six or seven. Some of my early memories of
wild-animal life are from the back hills of Monterey
County and the southern end of the Sierra in the Walker
Basin country. I recall watching a family of coyotes hunting, and remember spending long hours by a waterhole,
watching the game come down to drink. Once I found an
old bighorn skull in an area from which the wild sheep had
long before been exterminated. At another time it was the
thrill of finding the track of a black bear in an area where

* *The Roots of Heaven.* New York, Simon and Schuster, 1958.

no bears were supposed to exist. Once, coming over a rise in the early morning at Lake Lagunitas, I startled what I remember as sixty deer that ran off as a herd, waving a whole forest of antlers—a sight that I have not equaled since among the coast blacktailed deer. I spent years learning to identify every species of bird that I could find within the limits of San Francisco, and was fascinated by the great variety that existed there, almost unknown to most people. These early experiences in the field have remained far more vivid in memory than most of the more spectacular and dramatic sights I have encountered in later years.

Most of what is written about wild nature is read only by those who are already convinced of its importance. The rest of the public ignores it. Many people seem to care nothing for the wild animals except when these directly affect their own welfare. But at the other end of the scale, others find that the presence of wild animals so enriches their own existence that they could not contemplate a world without wildlife. Today people have a choice. They can be concerned with wild animals or they can ignore them. When California was first settled, there was not this choice. One could not ignore wildlife; it was a compelling factor of the environment. One could be for animals or against animals, but not indifferent. Most were against those things that were large and dangerous or small and poisonous, and in favor of those that were edible, strikingly beautiful, or both.

The Spanish settlers who first reached California were impressed by many of the strange aspects of the land and its inhabitants. In the journals of Pedro Fages, Juan Bautista de Anza, Miguel Costanso, and others of the early explorers there are frequent references to the wild animal life. "In this canyon were seen whole troops of bears" was written in the San Luis Obispo area. "We crossed it at a cost of three leagues' march, seeing on the way many herds of antelopes . . ." refers to the Santa Clara Valley. "Several soldiers requested permission to go hunting, as many deer had been seen," was written of the San Francisco area. Throughout the southern coastal region of California wildlife was present in abundance. To the Spanish soldier armed with eighteenth century weapons an encounter with a California grizzly, or the sight of the fresh tracks of a cougar, was no casual experience.

The early scene painted by the Spanish and later by the first American visitors is of incredible abundance of wildlife. The Central Valley sheltered herds of tule elk, pronghorn antelope, and black-tailed deer. A. B. Clarke, who visited it in 1852, writes: "I have no where seen game as plenty as in this valley. We killed an antelope in the morning. We could frequently see herds of deer and elk in different directions around us, as well as wild horses." Elk and antelope also roamed in abundance through the valley of the Salinas as far as Monterey, throughout the San Francisco Bay region, and in the valleys to the north. In the northern coastal area the Roosevelt elk took the place of the tule elk, and along with the black-tailed deer inhabited the glades and prairies in great numbers. In Humboldt County "Calvin Kinman states that one morning his father counted 40 bears in sight at once from a high point in the Mattole country, where he could overlook a great extent of open land. These are presumed to have been all, or nearly all, grizzlies, as Calvin Kinman states that black bears were not common in the range of the grizzly, and only seemed to appear in numbers as the latter was exterminated." *

John Muir was impressed with the abundance of the bighorn sheep in the lava-bed country north of Shasta, and of the many herds that occurred along the Sierra Nevada to its southern limits. Through the Mojave country and the mountains of Southern California a desert race of bighorn was also common. All the early visitors wrote of the coyote, whose yapping night song was to become the serenade of the early West. Where the great urban mass of Los Angeles now fills the landscape, Richard Henry Dana wrote in 1835, "The [coyotes] (a wild animal of a nature and appearance between that of the fox and the wolf) set up their sharp, quick bark, and two owls, at the end of two distant points running into the bay on different sides of the hill where I lay, kept up their alternate dismal notes." †
Later, anchored near the mouth of San Francisco Bay, Dana writes "under a high and beautifully sloping hill, on which herds of hundreds and hundreds of red deer and the stag (elk), with his high branching antlers, were bounding about, looking at us for a moment and then starting off affrighted at the noises which we made for the purpose of seeing the variety of their beautiful attitudes and motions."

Dominating the avian world was the giant condor, which thrived on the abundant carcasses of Spanish livestock. Early gold miners filled condor plumes with gold dust. Perhaps the most fascinating sight was the great mass of waterfowl, shore birds, and marsh birds that filled those marshes dominated by the tall bulrush, the tule, in the

* Joseph Grinnell, J. Dixon and J. Linsdale, *The Fur-Bearing Mammals of California* (Berkeley, University of California Press, 1937).
† *Two Years Before the Mast* (New York, Doubleday, 1949).

Central Valley. Here were birds in the tens of millons that darkened the sky when migrations sent them winging northward.

The thriving animal life attracted the fur trappers, Jed Smith and his Hudson's Bay Company crew, John Work's party, mountain men from Wyoming, and the Russians who pursued the sea otter down the California coast to the dismay of the Spanish military. The fur seekers trapped beaver on the Sacramento and ventured into far corners of the state beyond the knowledge of the Spanish. Their records portray a world far different than any that remains in California today.

One of the fascinating accounts of the early animal life is that of James C. "Grizzly" Adams, who roamed about the state with his two tamed grizzly bears, feeding on venison and panther meat. This colorful, if not entirely savory, character has left us with numerous records of true wolves, confirmed by some of the other early settlers. In his records one encounters the great slaughter that was overtaking the edible forms of game, and the poisoning campaign that was to decimate the carnivores.

It was inevitable that wildlife had to go from much of California. Grizzly bears cannot be raised in sheep pastures, nor are wolves welcome in the suburbs. Great herds of elk and antelope do not fit well into orchard or wheat field. But the manner and the thoroughness with which California's wildlife was destroyed are a blot on the record of the Americans. The Spanish seemed to live with the game without any great urge to slaughter it. The forty-niners and their followers were a different lot. Audubon and Bachman wrote, "Many of the miners, indeed, turned their attention to killing dear, elk, bear, antelopes, geese, ducks, and all sorts of game and wildfowl, by which they realized considerable sums from selling them at San Francisco." They mention one man who made $5,000 selling game meat to the miners in an eighteen-month period.

Van Dyke has left an account for the Central Valley: "The elk retreated from the open plains with the advent of the American, and hid in the vast tule swamps that covered hundreds of thousands of acres. Here they made great trails that ramified until lost in myriad mazes, while hogs that had gone wild made it extremely interesting for the hunter who dared enter on foot. . . . As it was impossible to see any distance even on horseback, and the mud was too thick for horses, the elk were quite safe for a time. But as the swamps began to be drained and the cover burned off, and roads made through the drying ground, it was again the same old story of the white man. By 1875 the antelope were a curiosity on the great plains, where so many thousands lately glimmered through the dancing heat, while the elk were almost as rare in the great tule swamps that so lately seemed inaccessible. By 1885 only one band was left, and that was on the immense ranch of Miller and Lux in the upper part of the valley, some twenty miles from Bakersfield." *

Starting with the mining camps of the Gold Rush, where the demand for meat seemed insatiable, market hunting became an important part of the California scene. Fresh meat, jerky, and hides were brought in from all parts of the state by men who found more profit in wildlife than in gold. Deer hides by the thousands were shipped from San Francisco. One group of hunters, operating in the Klamath Mountains, virtually exterminated the elk and drastically reduced the deer in that region. Waterfowl were

* From *The Deer Family*, by Theodore Roosevelt and others (New York, The Macmillan Company, 1902).

slaughtered and hauled off by the wagonload to the tables of San Francisco. The most destructive means of killing were used.

Remnant bands of elk held out in the dense forests of the northwest, and the herd of tule elk that Van Dyke described was preserved. During the 1920's the last pronghorn was killed in the Central Valley, and the species survived only in the Modoc-Siskiyou region in small numbers. The bighorns that John Muir had believed to be securely protected were exterminated from the lava beds and over much of their range. The wolf was nearly if not entirely wiped out. If any survive today it is in the rough, high-Sierra region where a few Sierra bighorn still look down from the high cliffs. The grizzly was hunted down as a bitter enemy until none survived anywhere. Writing from Humboldt County, H. E. Wilder said: "It was deemed enough if the trails could be made safe for the children to go to school, and if a reasonable proportion of the stock survived the Indians and wild animals in those hard times." *

Grouse and quail, ducks and geese, shorebirds and smaller creatures were ruthlessly shot out. In the mountains persistent trapping reduced the wolverine and fisher, marten, mink, and otter. From the streams most of the beaver were trapped out. Thus, throughout California, in the sixty years from 1850 to 1910, a massive faunal change, matched only by the postglacial extinctions, took place. Some species disappeared forever. The fauna that survived and finally regained lost ground was different from what had been in California before in the relative numbers and distribution of species. The way was thus paved for the

* Joseph Grinnell, J. Dixon and J. Linsdale, *The Fur-Bearing Mammals of California.*

wildlife problems that today trouble all people concerned with wild land and its management.

It was against this dismal background of mass slaughter and game scarcity that the game-conservation movement had its beginnings. The first Fish and Game Commission, when appointed by the governor, was charged with responsibility over the public heritage of wild animal life. The men who gave their time to this duty had a difficult, and apparently losing, fight. Lacking funds in sufficient quantity to accomplish anything, they could make recommendations and perhaps encourage the passage of protective laws for wildlife. But these laws meant nothing, and during the first thirty years of the commission's existence, wildlife continued to lose ground. It was not until 1907 that the legislature passed a bill requiring the purchase of a license by anyone who wished to hunt. The revenue from license sales went in part to hire game wardens, with both the power to enforce, and an interest in enforcing, game laws.

The first game wardens encountered people who felt that the state had no real authority to regulate the killing of game. Hunting was regarded by some as a natural right, not to be interfered with by the legislature. One of the first tasks of the wardens was the breaking up of market-hunting gangs. Since these men had a livelihood at stake, they were often not averse to shooting first when approached by a warden. Slowly, however, through sheer guts and persistence the wardens won public support. Gradually, each in his own area built up a little corps of people willing to join him in protecting the game. As more and more wardens were hired, as public opinion was influenced both by the game shortage and by educational programs, these groups of conservationists increased and spread, until

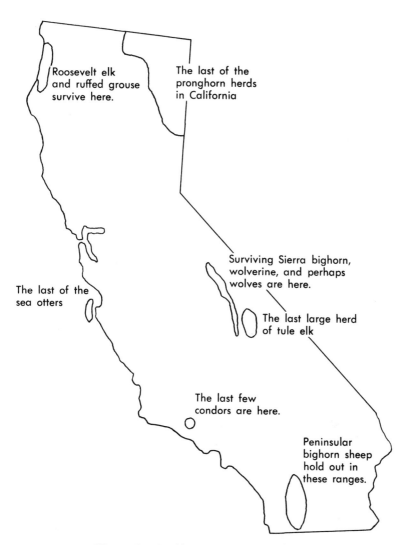

FIG. 5. Unrestricted killing and habitat changes brought the extinction of the grizzly, lava-beds bighorn, and sharp-tailed grouse in California. Many other species were reduced to a critically low level and have not since recovered much. In addition to those shown on this map, other, more widely distributed, animals, including the mountain lion, pine marten, and fisher, are also scarce today. *Source: Calif. Dept. of Fish and Game*

finally throughout the state a willingness to abide by game laws became a normal rather than an unusual attitude.

The story of wildlife conservation in California is marked by victories and some defeats, by unneeded feuding between those who should have been allies, and by peculiar contradictions. It is perhaps best illustrated by the story of the deer.

Shortly after the turn of the century, the deer herds of California were at a low ebb. Decimated by the unrestricted hunting of the past, they were hit by the unusually severe winters from 1879 until after 1900. Snow packs built up on high summer ranges, restricting their use to a short summer period. On critical winter ranges, where food is always a problem, snow piled deep, forcing the animals from favored feeding grounds and causing severe mortality. Beginning in the 1920's, or in some sections earlier, the weather ameliorated. At the same time the game laws protecting deer began to have some effective enforcement. Confronting those deer that had survived was a great area of excellent habitat, created by those very forces that had been most destructive to other resources, fire and logging, for example. On cutover or burned-over forests, new brush fields sprouted, providing choice food for the browsing deer. Once-overgrazed ranges, when livestock numbers were cut back, were invaded by such excellent deer foods as bitterbrush and mountain mahogany, far preferable for a deer than the bunch grasses of an earlier time. The deer began a rapid increase.

The extent of recovery of the deer herds was first hinted at early in the 1920's, when the California National Forest (now Mendocino) carried out an actual count of deer coming out in the evening to feed on glades or meadows. From this count the population in the forest was estimated at

40,000 animals. Few paid attention to this figure, but continued to provide against deer scarcity. Then in 1923 a chain of circumstances began that were once more to reveal the abundance of deer. Hoof-and-mouth disease, introduced accidentally into the state by a ship from Japan, spread through livestock herds and became established in the deer herd of the Stanislaus National Forest in the Sierra. When the first infected mule deer were found in the area north of Yosemite, all of those concerned with California's livestock industry were badly scared. Moving among the deer herds, hoof-and-mouth disease could, in theory, become permanently established and spread through the entire West. The decision was made to exterminate the infected deer. On the basis of available information, it was thought that at most a population of a few thousand animals was involved. Control operations were set up; poison stations using strychnine and salt were established. Next, hunters were moved in until finally 43 separate camps, with 3 to 10 hunters in each, were in operation. One thousand square miles of mountain country were combed over for deer. Instead of the few thousand suspected to be in the area, over 22,000 were known to have been killed. Of these, somewhat more than 10 percent were judged to be infected with the disease. When the shooting was called off, in 1926, no infected deer had been taken for nine months. However, the deer were far from exterminated. Within a few years their numbers in the area were reported to be back to normal.

These two early censuses established certain facts. One was that California's deer were not in any danger of extinction. Another was that people, even when quite familiar with the area involved, usually underestimated the numbers of deer.

By the 1930's deer populations over most of California had obviously recovered from their previously low levels. In most places deer were far more abundant than they had ever been before, because there was more and better deer habitat than in earlier days. Farmers who once used to stop work and call their friends if a deer appeared anywhere on the horizon now began to complain of damage by the ever-growing hordes of hungry animals. Deer descended from brushy hills to feed on orchards, row crops, and grain. A survey of damage conducted during the 1930's indicated that it was severe. It was to increase until for some ranchers and farmers it became intolerable. Government foresters and lumber companies found that deer were preventing the establishment of the tree crops on which their sustained-yield logging programs must depend. By the 1940's it was apparent that California was stocked and overstocked with deer numbering well over a million.

Unfortunately, California was not psychologically prepared for a problem involving too many deer. For many years the public education program had emphasized the scarcity of these animals and the need for strict protection. Among all the organized sportsmen, anyone who would shoot a doe was considered beneath contempt (although unorganized poachers continued to do so without a qualm). Waves of sympathy for the soft-eyed deer had been set in motion, and beat against the hearts of the conservation-minded public. Suddenly to turn off this feeling, to point to the need for heavier hunting and for reduction in the deer herds, was a task too great for the Fish and Game Department.

To add to the problem, the Department of Fish and Game found itself split down the middle. On one side were the biologists and managers, mostly technically trained people. On the other side were the old-time game wardens, hatchery men, and state trappers, who had fought the battle against game scarcity too long suddenly to change sides. Truth may have been on the side of the biologist, but practical politics favored the warden, who had been "Mr. Fish and Game" to the local people in almost every county.

Basically the biologists sought to establish a system of deer-herd regulation, by which the number of animals to be shot from any area would depend on the annual rate of production of the deer in that area. In order to hold numbers of deer in check and tailor the deer herds to fit the capacity of the range, it was held to be necessary to shoot both bucks and does. In a polygamous population where some of the males always escape the hunter, shooting bucks only will not control a population. But doe shooting ran contrary to California tradition, and in every village and town a controversy went on. Meetings between Fish and Game managers, supported by local farmers, and the sportsmen, sometimes supported behind the scenes by the local warden, often ended in near violence.

Little by little the deer-management program made gains. The first doe shoot was carried out on neutral ground, on Catalina Island, in 1949. It went off without trouble. In the following years "special" hunts were held in problem areas to accustom the public gradually to the hunting of does. Finally, in 1956, feeling full of confidence, the Department of Fish and Game decided to throw most of the state open to "antlerless" deer hunting. The proposal touched off an explosion. Diehard sportsmen rallied to the cause, swearing that no does would die in X County, Y County, or Z County. When the hunt was carried through despite the objections, no shortage of doe shooters was to be seen in the field. However, the next year a wave of revolt among the organized sportsmen was carried to the legislature. As a result the Fish and Game Commission lost its right to establish antlerless deer seasons without local, county supervisor's, approval. Since 1957 deer-management gains have mostly been in a reverse direction. Some of the problem deer herds, which could have been maintained at a reasonable level, have provided their own answer to the question by dying off.

The deer-management controversy brought to light a division that had occurred among the conservationists. On one side were the biologists of the Fish and Game department, the sportsmen who were willing to study and understand the situation, and a large segment of the interested public. Also on this side, however, were aligned stockmen, farmers, foresters, and lumber-company executives and those owners of suburban gardens who had seen too many deer among their rosebushes. Unfortunately this group of supporters included many who would be content to shoot the last deer in California in order to be free from any danger of damage. On the other side were sportsmen who doubted the results of the Fish and Game department's studies including many who couldn't read or understand them; some employees of the department, a number of people who favored wildlife but opposed hunting, and a section of people who opposed killing animals at any time for any purpose.

On the one side the accusation of "management madness" could be leveled. There were some who wanted to convert wild animals into the likeness of domestic herds, carefully tended and cropped. This, while justifiable on some lands and under some circumstances, was not likely to win support from those who wanted to feel that they had won their trophy animals from some wild herd in a rough and remote area. Nor could it win support from the advocates of wilderness and natural preserves, who did not want to see deer "harvesters" building access roads into their sanctuaries. On the other side were many who sought only to use the Department of Fish and Game as a target for their own political advantage, and many who seemed unable to realize that wild animals seldom live to a ripe old age, and if protected from the hunter are bound to fall victim to something equally violent or cruel. Between these divergent attitudes there is hope that in time a moderate point of view will prevail, that the excess of deer in the state will be used to provide hunting for those who enjoy the sport but, at the same time, will be managed in accordance with Aldo Leopold's rule, that the recreational value of game is inverse to the management effort expended upon it.

Since the first hunting licenses went on sale in 1907, the California Department of Fish and Game has been supported entirely by revenue obtained from licenses and fees paid by those who were using the fish-and-game resource. The Fish and Game department, supervised by the commission, has therefore become self-sustaining, neither drawing upon the general treasury nor dependent upon the vagaries of a legislature at budget time. However, because the money comes from the sportsmen and commercial fishermen these groups have felt, justifiably, a proprietary interest in the state fish-and-game agency. Furthermore they have been alert and active in protecting their interests. The department in turn has in some ways behaved as though it existed to serve the licensed hunters and fishermen primarily. This had led in turn to an interest in game animals only, rather than wildlife in general. It has led also to an emphasis on those kinds of game of immediate concern to the sportsman in his annual hunting effort, to the neglect of other species. Deer and ducks, quail and pheasants became important, and most research and management money went toward the enhancement of their numbers. Bighorn and wolverine, ruffed grouse and orioles were considered much less important. Anything rare, remote, or unable to respond quickly to management has been to some degree neglected. Consequently, although some species of wildlife are exceedingly abundant, others have made no gains since they were initially reduced in numbers by excessive exploitation. For this the department is not entirely to be blamed. It has gone in the direction that the vocal segment of its public demanded. The sportsmen are not to be blamed for protecting their own interests. Indifference or inactivity on the part of the general public who should have been interested, but were not, is the cause.

The bitter controversies that have raged over such questions as the management of deer, and equally bitter ones that have followed concerning the pheasants, ducks, trout, and salmon, have tended to create a defensive mentality among some of the employees of the Fish and Game Department. This leads to a tendency to retreat before being attacked, to leave a position carefully established by research, and occupy some halfway ground that is untenable, to pull punches and tell only half of the truth about a situation. Many groups have failed to support the department because of a feeling that they had not been told the entire story, but only what the department felt that they needed to know. One of the first requisites for a successful wildlife program is a Fish and Game department free from political pressures, able to go ahead and do the job of conservation to the best of its ability, using the best knowledge available. But in California there is such persistent interference on the part of the legislature, pushed often by special-interest lobbyists, that the Fish and Game department must ask "What can we get by with?" rather than "What should be done?"

Perhaps I feel too strongly on this issue because of the responsibility I have had for the training of students in wildlife management. It is discouraging to send out, year after year, graduates trained in the scientific principles and techniques of wildlife biology, and know that only rarely, in California, will they be able to see their knowledge translated into positive action in the field. It is discouraging to know that competent men will be frustrated by public indifference, entrenched ignorance, and unwarranted legislative interference. Some students have decided to select a different field of work after attending just one sportsmen's meeting. There are few groups of public servants more dedicated to the public interest than the biologists, managers, and wardens of wildlife departments. Yet few groups suffer more from attacks on their personal intelligence and integrity. Where wildlife is concerned, every layman is his own physician.

There is much that should be done in California to restore the richness and variety that wild animal populations can add to life within the state. Antelope and elk need to be restored over a much broader area of range than they now occupy. The bighorn sheep need careful attention if they are to regain their former range. Little is known about the kind of management needed to build up numbers of grouse to a reasonable level of abundance. Although waterfowl are still numerous, many species are still scarce, and little is done to increase them. New dangers are always appearing as more and more land and water are devoted to purposes incompatible with wildlife conservation. The widespread use of poisons for the control of agricultural pests has created a grave danger for all wild animals, large and small. Predatory mammals and birds havs been reduced to a point of scarcity in most parts of the state in the pretense of protecting already abundant game animals, or for the encouragement of sheep grazing, often in regions from which it had best be excluded.

One cannot ask that the wildlife of California be restored to what it was in Spanish times. But one can request that the greatest variety of wild animals that can be supported, without danger to other resources, be brought back to every area of the state where such restoration is still possible. One can ask that wildlife be considered when land-use planning and water planning are conducted and that wildlife be given its fair share. The aim of wildlife conservation in California should not be the production of maximum bags of a few kinds of game sought after by hunters, but the restoration of wildlife variety to enrich the lives of each person in the state. It should mean as much attention to songbirds in city gardens as to mallards on public hunting grounds, to mountain lions in wilderness as to pheasants on valley farms. There are large segments of the public who will be willing to support a program aimed truly at wildlife conservation who do not back a program aimed only at increasing shootable game.

Anyone who has not been blind to the world around him knows that life for people can be enriched by the presence of wild creatures in man's environment. The enjoyment of watching wild animals in wild places adds a savor to life, even if it is but a casual encounter. The knowledge that wild nature still exists adds a dimension of freedom to an otherwise restricted life—leaves open the possibility for escape from the narrow confinements of civilization. If we create in California a world with no space left for wild animals, it will prove to be a world with little space for human freedom.

FOUR

THE PRAIRIES
THAT VANISHED

As sheep advance, flowers, vegetation, grass,
soil, plenty, and poetry vanish. —JOHN MUIR *

Range managers are pictured by those who try to
advertise the profession as cowboy types in high-heeled
boots, riding fine horses across the prairie wild. In actuality,
most of them spend most time crawling on hands and
knees, trying to determine the species of a grass already
three-quarters eaten by some cow, or trying to estimate, by
various refined techniques, the production and use of forage
in some pasture. Yet most of them were attracted to their
profession by their liking for an outdoor life combined with
a scientific bent and a strange attraction toward those kinds
of domestic animals known as whitefaces, Brahmans, short-
horns, or Aberdeen-Angus. My brother was led into the
profession through his early childhood desire to be a cowboy, but after only a brief career in that line of work he
found himself in time measuring the length of grass blades,

* *John of the Mountains*. Linnie Marsh Wolfe. Houghton Mifflin, Boston, 1938.

and calculating browsing on twigs. His interest in range-lands eventually was to lead him to an unexpected career in wildlife management, since deer and elk also eat grass and browse on twigs. My desire, on the other hand, to study wild animals led me in time to find myself crawling up and down brushy ridges to find out how much food it took to support a deer, and, although not strongly attracted toward beef cattle, eventually to at least part-time involvement in the range-management profession.

Whatever their original inclination, range and wildlife managers alike, along with many foresters, find themselves involved in the task of keeping California's rangelands green and productive, yielding meat from cattle and sheep along with all of those other benefits that wild lands can give to the people. To do this job it is necessary to find out first what the rangelands were like before the European colonist and his grazing livestock were to enter the scene.

Once there were fields of grass waving tall in the wind as far as the eye could see. The Spanish travelers came and described them—the finest pasture, an abundance of pasture, enough for all the flocks and herds, they said. They were not good at describing a countryside, but they knew what they were interested in, and a land that could support livestock had much appeal. They brought their cattle and sheep, their horses and mules, and with them they brought their camp followers, the weedy plants that had followed them already halfway around the world. They began a process of change and a devastation that was left to us as a legacy. William Brewer saw the change in 1864, following the great drought: "Our road lay over the mountains. They are perfectly dry and barren, no grass—here and there a poor gaunt cow is seen, but what she gets to eat is very mysterious . . . The ride was over the plain, which is utterly bare of herbage. No green thing greets the eye, and clouds of dust fill the air. Here and there are carcasses of cattle, but we see few living ones." * The needle grasses and wild rye disappeared and we were left with foxtail and Medusa's head. The June grass, bluegrass, and poppies have gone. We have inherited the poverty grass, tarweed, and thistle.

Apart from being major feats of pioneering travel, the journeys of Anza across the Mojave to the new mission at San Diego were noteworthy in another way. They brought the first large numbers of livestock to California to supplement the small herd brought north from Baja California. Thus was established the beginnings of an industry that was to dominate the economy of the country for more than a century and in the process change the face of the land. California was to become in time the land of the *vaquero* and *caballero* who counted his wealth in the productivity of his herds and flocks. The descendants of the first horses and cattle, burros, sheep and goats were to spread widely and increase over all of the Spanish lands. Horses and cattle, in time, were to escape from captivity and move into areas where Spanish settlement did not penetrate, roaming in great herds among the elk and antelope of the Central Valley. The burro was to move into the desert regions and establish itself as a permanent wild resident. Feral goats were to occupy the heights of the offshore islands. The combined effects of the tamed and wild livestock were to change the nature of the California rangelands, to destroy the old California prairie, and replace the native plants with alien species. This was the first major destruction of

* *Up and Down California in 1860–1864* (Berkeley, University of California Press, 1949).

the wild lands of California to be charged against the influence of the white man.

There is hardly a field ecologist or range manager alive who does not wish that somewhere among the early Spanish colonists there had been a competent botanist or any person with a keen interest in the vegetation of the land. The journals that have been left behind show no such interest. The Spanish saw the country with the eyes of a prospective colonist, and were not much interested in wild nature. Pasturage was plentiful, their journals state. But what was growing there? They left no record. We have since found that the original rangeland of California was covered by native species of plants, evolved in North America, distinct from those of other lands. We also know that most of the plants to be found on those same rangelands now are aliens, mostly invaders from the Mediterranean lands of Europe. To learn what the rangelands once were and how they have changed has taken some highly expert detective work. We still do not know why the change was so complete. Elsewhere in North America nothing quite so striking has taken place.

To find what once grew in California, students of plants and rangelands have sought for areas that have somehow escaped the change. Such places are difficult to find. The search for forage has taken livestock with their herders into the most out-of-the-way places. Even small offshore islands in bays and off the coast, where the amount of grass to be eaten would hardly seem to justify the effort of getting to it, were stocked with domestic animals. Still, a few areas either escaped the punishment of excessive grazing or have recovered from it. Old fenced graveyards, railroad rights-of-way, and some protected parts of the more carefully tended ranches have provided some information. Studies

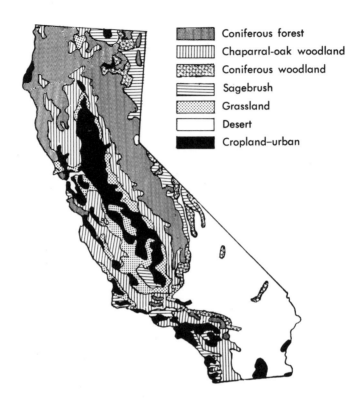

▨	Coniferous forest
▥	Chaparral-oak woodland
▨	Coniferous woodland
☰	Sagebrush
▦	Grassland
☐	Desert
■	Cropland–urban

FIG. 6. California's vegetation. Even on this simplified map the complexity of the vegetation pattern is obvious. Each mountain and valley, slope or exposure provides a somewhat different environment in which different combinations of plants thrive. California's grassland, once one of the most widespread kinds of vegetation, has suffered the greatest encroachment from agricultural and urban development.

of the process of change on existing ranges, under varying degrees of grazing or in its absence, have produced other information. From this it has been determined that the original grasslands of the Central Valley and coastal mountains of California were once covered with stands of perennial grasses, mostly of the bunchgrass form growing in tufts or clumps. These held the ground year after year despite the vagaries of the climate and the pressure from native wild animals. The species of grasses that grew in California have names that are too unfamiliar to most people: needle grass, June grass, and wild rye; oat grass and oniongrass. Growing with them were the variety of wild flowers that painted the hills golden or purple in the spring: the California poppy and buttercup; lupines and larkspur, mariposa lilies and wild iris. Together they formed a community of plants with a remarkably high grazing capacity, and in the more humid parts of the state one that was perhaps the most productive rangeland in North America. There were some 22,000,000 acres of the old California prairie. In addition an even larger acreage of rangeland included areas that were dominated by trees or shrubs but supported an understory of grass. Under a reasonable degree of management this rangeland could have continued to support a high number of livestock for centuries on end. But, like most rangelands in the pathway of Western man, it received no management at all until almost too late.

To discover how the prairies came to be invaded and occupied by exotic weeds has taken a particularly neat piece of scientific detection. The old missions and other buildings were made for the most part with bricks formed from the adobe mud that is common in coastal California. To bind these bricks, grass straw was used, presumably being obtained from whatever field of grass was handiest to the building site. George W. Hendry and his coworkers have carefully examined and identified the species of plants contained in these old adobes; knowing the date when the structure was built, they have pieced together a history of the invasion of California by alien plants. It was evident that some species arrived with the first settlers, perhaps in the wool of sheep, in hay carried on ships for livestock feed, or in the droppings of domestic animals. These could readily have established themselves on the disturbed ground around the fields cleared for farming, or on trampled places near the missions and settlements. There they could hold on until conditions permitted their spread into the area held by native vegetation on the open range.

The spread of exotic weeds and grasses was favored by the nature of the California climate. Since summer drought is the rule, winter rainfall must be adequate to support the spring growth of plants. In a normal year this is true, but a normal year is as rare as a normal human being. Some years are dry, others wet. Minor changes in rainfall have little effect but there have also been major changes. Thus, François Matthes, the geologist and student of glaciers, has found evidence that all the mountain glaciers disappeared in California during a relatively warm, dry period before the thirteenth century of the Christian Era. This was the period during which the Vikings colonized Greenland and found forests growing where now the ground is permanently frozen. From the thirteenth century until almost the end of the Spanish period in California, the climate was cooler, and more moist than now, and snowfall averaged higher. Matthes termed this period a "little ice age," and believed that it was marked by a buildup of the mountain glaciers of the Sierra. Since 1850, however, the climate has been more warm and dry, except for a brief return to cool, wet conditions in the decades around the turn of the century. However, within this framework of major climatic trends there have been up-and-down cycles of drought and humidity. Early in the nineteenth century, south-coastal California was struck by some severe droughts. One, lasting from 1828 to 1830, was said to be a time when no rain fell for twenty-two months in coastal Southern California. Such a drought must have had a crippling effect upon the vegetation, and would have created a serious overgrazing problem. It was after this that some of the exotic grasses and weeds spread widely. Edwin Bryant noted the widespread abundance of the alien wild oat and yellow mustard when he came to California in the middle 1830's.

Nearly all the grasses and weeds that invaded California were annuals. Each year, after setting seed, they died. The seeds, buried in the dust or litter, could resist drought, for long periods if necessary, and be ready to germinate when rains finally came. Thus annuals are able to persist

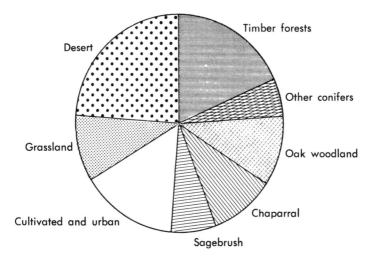

FIG. 7. Relative proportions of land occupied by various vegetation types in California. Today, sagebrush, oak woodland, and grassland provide most of the space for livestock grazing. *Source: U.S. Forest Service*

in deserts, and are apt to spread during drought cycles. Perennial plants can resist drought if deeply rooted and in touch with underground water supplies. Some have special drought-resisting specializations. Others, however, do not hold up well to prolonged drought. All are handicapped by heavy grazing in their ability to stand up to drought. Thus the combination of heavy grazing and dry cycles paved the way for widespread invasions by exotic annual plants. The waves of invasion moved from south to north. The grasslands of Northern California were spared the early impact of Spanish livestock, and did not begin to change until after the American colonists arrived on the scene.

The livestock of early California were for the most part a small, leggy, long-horned breed of Spanish cattle, and a small, long-legged sheep of mixed ancestry called a *churro*. These beasts had little to recommend them except hardiness, but they were tough and could thrive and increase under difficult conditions on the range. With a little neglect the cattle could become wilder than the elk that they joined in the valley ranges. As the Spanish mission holdings spread northward toward Sonoma, and the missions claimed much of the land in coastal California, the numbers of livestock increased phenomenally. Various estimates place the numbers of livestock at the height of the mission period at close to 400,000 head of cattle, and 300,000 sheep. In addition there were large numbers of horses and mules in tamed herds, and perhaps even more living as wild mustangs.

In dry years the wild stock was slaughtered in attempts to save the forage for the mission herds. During the 1828–1830 drought livestock died off in droves, and it has been estimated that 40,000 cattle and horses perished. Before they died they must have consumed most of the available forage. The numbers of animals bounced back quickly after the rains returned, and by Gold Rush days all classes of livestock were again abundant in Spanish California. Under the economic conditions found in early California it was quantity rather than quality of animals that paid off. The local demand for meat was small, and could be met easily. Most of the livestock that were marketed were sold only for hides or tallow. Ships from many nations, such as the one that Richard Henry Dana described in his *Two Years Before the Mast*, put in at the growing ports of San Diego, Monterey, and San Francisco to load vast quantities of hides and tallow. There was no market for quality beef animals, and the sheep that were available were incapable of producing fine-quality wool.

The late 1840's saw the decline of Mexican influence on California, culminating in the madness of the Gold Rush. The instability of the times and the demand for meat in the goldfields and the burgeoning cities brought depletion of the existing herds, and led to the movement of trail herds from Texas and the Middle West into California. These built the foundation for a major increase in livestock in the decade of the 1850's, despite the uncertainty over land-ownership that followed the breakup of the old Spanish system. During this decade, domestic animals increased more than fivefold, to over a million head of cattle and an equal number of sheep. But, once more, disaster in the form of the uncertain California climate struck the industry. By 1862, when cattle had boomed to over 3,000,000 head, the state experienced an almost unbelievably heavy rainfall. Flood waters poured down the rivers of the Sierra and north coast, carrying with them the silt and debris from the mining operations. Rains hit the California rangelands and scoured soil from overgrazed slopes. A vast lake, estimated by some to equal the size of Lake Michigan, but fortunately not the depth, filled the Sacramento Valley, leaving most of the new state capital well submerged. It is estimated that hundreds of thousands of cattle drowned. Ironically enough, the flood was followed by the two most severe drought years for which weather records are available. From 1862 to 1864 little rain fell in California. The little grass that grew was quickly consumed by hungry animals. Perhaps a million head of livestock, mostly cattle, perished in the state, and the once-productive rangelands presented the picture of dust and desolation described by William Brewer earlier in this chapter. Stockmen, desperate for forage to keep their animals alive, moved up into the mountains, establishing for the first time the pattern of migratory grazing. They moved east of the Sierra to establish themselves in the Owens Valley, and even out into the Mojave Desert. Although the winter of 1864 and 1865 brought the rains once more, many of the cattlemen lost heart. Cattle numbers continued to decline to a low of half a million in 1870, one-sixth of the numbers that were present at the peak.

The sheepmen profited by the blow to the cattle industry. Sheep require less water and can more readily be herded about to follow the forage supply. It is estimated that the number of sheep increased to a peak of 5,500,000 head by 1875. The day of the migratory sheepherder, usually from the Basque country of Spain, had arrived in California. Great trail herds of sheep were wintered in areas of favorable climate. One of the great centers, in the mountains south of Bakersfield, still shows the scars from the sheep concentrations of these days. From these wintering grounds the sheep were moved out in spring, following trails up the east side of the Sierra Nevada, then working over the mountain passes in summer, and moving slowly back through the mountain meadows as the year progressed. The passage of one migratory band after another brought devastation to the high country. John Muir, who worked at sheepherding when he first came to California, wrote in blistering terms of the damage that was done to the country that is now in the Yosemite.

Throughout the entire period of the livestock boom, from 1850 until the peak was passed in the 1870's, the stockman was favored by the philosophy of landownership and use that prevailed. The early state legislature of California passed a "no-fence" law that required private landowners to assume responsibility for protecting their own property through fencing. The landlord had no redress against trespassing livestock unless he had built a stock-proof fence. Since this was before the days of barbed wire, and fencing materials were scarce and expensive, it was a foolhardy soul who attempted to farm in the range country. Much of the state was publicly owned, and here initially there was no attempt at control. A man who had some claim to the ownership of a stream or spring, and thus controlled the water supply, could exercise a monopoly over the grazing of vast acreages of public land. Little investment was required to get into the grazing business—just enough money to buy up a herd of animals, and access to the public domain. Some even skipped this requirement by use of the "long rope" principle, roping and branding the young animals from someone else's herd. Through one means or another, great livestock empires were built up, such as the holdings of Miller and Lux, who controlled some 500,000 acres of California land.

During the days of the livestock boom, Southern California was the center of the industry. Los Angeles was known as a "cow county," and proud of this designation. But the increasing demand for the better lands by farmers, the growth of the population, and the deterioration of the rangelands in general brought an end to the boom. The 1860's saw an end to the "no-fence" law, and the fixing of the responsibility for trespass upon the stockman. The 1870's saw the spread of the railroads, making possible the shipment of farm produce quickly to market. The 1880's saw great numbers of immigrants arrive and land values begin to grow out of reach of stock raisers. The 1890's saw an end to the old free access to the publicly owned ranges of the mountains.

By the time the California livestock industry had reached its peak and begun to decline, great damage had already been done to the rangelands. It has been estimated by range experts of the United States Forest Service and the California Division of Forestry that the grazing capacity of the California ranges was cut in half through overgrazing, soil erosion, and the invasion of low-quality annual weeds and grasses. The change was so complete that in some places we no longer can surmise the nature of the original plant cover. The better-quality annual grasses that first invaded throughout the state were replaced in each succeeding decade by species of still lower quality, until in some places all that was left was worthless tarweed, star thistle, or cheat grass. Today, in many parts of the state there is no hope of bringing back the native perennial grasses; ranges are managed only to maintain the better-quality exotic annuals.

The reasons for the destruction of the California ranges are various. Many of the Spanish herders had inherited the old careless practices of range management that had once

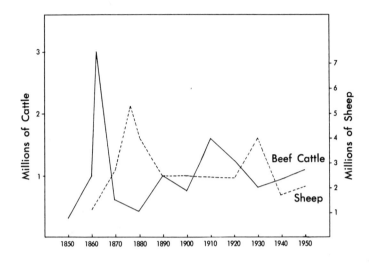

FIG. 8. Cattle numbers in California reached a peak before the drought of 1862–1864. Following the die-off among cattle, many stockmen shifted to sheep. The rangelands have not recovered from the damage caused by the excessive grazing pressure of these early days. The graph shows numbers of cattle and sheep on California ranges. *Source: Burcham,* California Range Land, *1957*

characterized the Mesta, the sheepowners' associations that destroyed the rangelands in much of Spain. There was little incentive for careful control of livestock in the early days when animal values were low. There was no knowledge about the requirements for proper range management. The erratic climate of California made the grasslands less able to stand up to abuse. Along the north coast, where the rainfall was higher, damage was much less, and recovery has been much more easy to accomplish. But the nature of the grasses themselves was in part responsible for the damage. California did not support the tough, grazing-resistant sod-formers, such as the buffalo grasses and grama grasses that have held out so well in the Great

Plains region. The invading annuals were too well adapted to the California range, coming as they did from Mediterranean lands with similar soils and climate, and conditioned as they were to centuries of livestock grazing. Finally, the breakup of the landownership pattern and the lack of control over the publicly owned range added the final touch of destruction.

The old range livestock industry has gone from California, and in its place a new one has arisen, occupying the still extensive grazing lands of the state. Its importance to the economy of the state is still great, for we have yet to find a way to produce beef or lamb, pork or milk in chemical factories, and sheep-grown wool is still preferred by many over the synthetic fibers. It is still more economical to produce livestock on relatively low-value rangelands than it is to devote better-quality farming land to this purpose; range feed costs less than hay. However, the new livestock industry is seldom entirely independent from the farming and pasture lands of the better soils. The ranges seldom are called upon to support grazing animals through the year, as they once did. Now supplemental feed, grown on the valley lands, carries the animals through more critical periods, and most animals are fattened in valley feed lots before they appear in the market. Quality of beef and wool have become all important, encouraging careful husbandry. When each calf marketed brings a hundred dollars or more in income, the owner pays attention to the health and condition of his breeding herd. But despite the improved economic incentives, the livestock business seldom brings extravagant profits, and range-management problems remain.

Over many areas of the state ranges continue to deteriorate. Gullies still eat into overgrazed slopes, and the winds blow soil from lands ground into dust by too many hooves. The scars of a century ago have yet to be fully repaired. Too frequently the landownership pattern is a cause. Except on the best lands, livestock production requires large acreages to be economically feasible. A rancher who measures his acreage in the hundreds often cannot afford to do a good job, and the temptation to overstock in order to build up the margin of profit is great. Only those who measure their holdings in thousands of acres can afford to stock at conservative levels and plow money back into the land for the improvements that will bring increased profit tomorrow. But large holdings are difficult to acquire when land prices are high. Ultimately the small rancher will fail, but in the process the range and soil will also fail.

Consideration of a few individual ranches will illustrate the present problem. One large ranch of 24,000 acres has been often used as an example of range improvement. It was overgrazed by sheep for many years, and the original native grasses had been replaced to a large extent by a worthless weed cover of Medusa head. When the ownership changed, the sheep were replaced by cattle, and stocking was reduced to a conservative level. A system of rotation grazing was instituted that allowed the better grasses to reseed and establish themselves each year on some of the pastures. With this kind of management the more valuable annual grasses and the native perennial grasses began to recover. As the range improved over a ten-year period, it became possible to boost both the rate of stocking and the annual income while still allowing for further improvement. At the present time, the trend is still upward. However, the new owner brought in capital that had been earned in other areas from other lines of business. Had he been chained to the sheep business like the previous owner, he would have found it difficult to raise money for improvements or withstand the financial loss brought by a decrease in animal numbers.

Not far from this ranch is a 1,700-acre holding that has also been improved. Here, too, the owner has other sources of income, and is not dependent upon his livestock for his sole support. A change from cattle to sheep, the construction of fences, and the provision of some supplemental feed has brought marked gains in the grazing capacity of the ranch that will, in the end, pay off in increased profits. But the improvement could not have been financed from profits that could have been earned from the land alone. This ranch was too small to allow for improvements from any rancher forced to make a living from it.

In the same general area other ranches continue to go downhill. Some are on a decline because they are not large enough to be workable economic units, some because of absentee or divided ownership, and consequent lack of interest in what happens to the range. Others are units leased out without restriction on grazing practices. Still others belong to people who are simply exploiting them through maximum stocking for an immediate profit, with no concern for their future condition. The public, in the long run, will suffer from the deterioration of these rangelands. Damage to the range leads to damage to soil and watershed conditions and to the future of the communities involved. But the public has no say in the management of these lands. There are no laws on the books controlling the use of private ranges. It is still entirely legal to destroy the land. There are few rewards, and there is no glory for the good manager.

It is relatively easy to promote public interest in many

phases of conservation. Rugged wilderness country is spectacular and has its devoted protectors. The larger species of wild animals, or the more glamorous ones, have hosts of defenders. Forests have their friends, and even individual species of trees have organizations to protect them. But it is difficult to find friends for grass. Grasses look too much alike to the uninitiated, and at times even baffle the student. An overgrazed range will look greener than one that is properly managed. A weedy brome grass or an introduced pasture grass sways nicely in the wind, and none but the expert knows that it does not belong in the natural scene. Of the original kinds of forest in California, we can find representative tracts that have been preserved, but of the many kinds of native grassland there is little remaining. We have no grassland reserves or primitive areas, and most of us don't even know what a good range should look like. Even in state and national parks the grasslands are often allowed to deteriorate or grow up in alien species without anyone being aware of the change. Yet natural grasslands are surely as valuable from a scientific viewpoint as natural forests. We should at least have the opportunity to see a few fragments of the old prairie, and know how it once felt underfoot. We might find that such areas have great aesthetic value, if we could only be permitted to see one. Such native grasslands could have extreme value to the soil scientist, the watershed expert, and particularly to the range manager. They could serve as standards against which to measure management efforts, or to use as management goals. The very few that are left in California should be saved. Elsewhere, through careful, constructive management, others could be restored. The benefits for the future, even in this land-hungry state, would justify the costs.

FIVE

LAND OF THE
TALL TIMBER

Any fool can destroy trees. They cannot defend themselves or run away. —JOHN MUIR *

ALTHOUGH not an island, California has many of the
characteristics of one. Cut off by desert and steppe from the
higher rainfall areas of the east, it has developed many
unique features. Its bird fauna is distinctive; it has many
unusual kinds of mammals. Species and ways of life that
would have difficulty surviving elsewhere can find some
small refuge on a mountaintop or a coastal peninsula, and
remain alive. In its forests, in particular, the state has a
great variety of unusual trees. Most striking to many are
the pines, which include not just the few species usually
encountered elsewhere, but a large number of forms, some
with extremely limited distribution. The state also provides the last home of the magnificent redwood and its
ancient relative the Big Tree. Among the other strange
species it has such things as the Catalina ironwood, the
Washington palm, California nutmeg, Santa Lucia fir,

* *John of the Mountains.*

Monterey and dwarf cypresses. These are uniquely Californian.

Forests of evergreen conifers once covered more than 21,000,000 acres, more than one-fifth of the state, in a mixture of pine, fir, spruce, redwood, and Douglas fir. More than 10,000,000 acres were covered with woodland, dominated mostly by oaks, but containing also many other trees well known in the forests of the east: maple, ash, walnut, sycamore, and willow. The state also has some 3,500,000 acres of open coniferous woodland, dominated by the drought-enduring juniper and the piñon pine.

The great sweeps of country covered by yellow pine, redwood, or Douglas fir are most impressive to the commercially minded lumberman, but to a person with a more general interest in plant life, the odd little remnant groves of forests that were once more widespread are more fascinating. Thus, high in the White Mountains at more than 10,000 feet is an ancient grove of bristle-cone pines, thought to be among the oldest trees in the world. How they have survived the vicissitudes of climatic change and geological stress during the many centuries they have endured in this barren habitat is a question that baffles many. But there is little doubt that the shaggy trees look like some ancient survivors from the past. One expects to find some strange kind of animal living there, but in this they are a disappointment. Only the forest belongs to the past. Across the Sierras from these are the last surviving groves of the Big Trees, containing specimens that have stood for more than 4,000 years and are up to 27 feet in diameter. These trees, squat and heavy rather than tall and graceful, are frankly unbelievable. They cannot be described adequately, and most photographs seem to just miss. After driving through groves of pine trees big enough from any human standpoint, an encounter with these monsters produces a shock. They belong with the world of mammoths and ground sloths.

But it is not only the ancient or the large trees that are fascinating. It is wonderful to see the cypresses that survive only in the Monterey-Carmel area and occur as natives nowhere else in the world. Their tortured, twisted trunks bear witness to their struggle with wind and salt spray from the ocean over many long decades. They have been forced to this last refuge by the competition with other species, better adapted to survive on the soils of the plains and mountains farther from the coast. But on their windswept refuge they have successfully fought off their rivals and made a last stand. Not far from them is an extensive area dominated by dark Monterey-pine forest, one of the few naturally occurring groves left in the world—the others are also on the coast or islands of central and Southern California. This surprising tree, already reduced to remnant stands when California was first discovered, is now one of the most widespread timber trees in the world. It is capable of rapid growth, and can produce good-quality softwood timber. In Australia, South Africa, and other countries it has been planted over thousands of acres in plantations that dominate the landscape and yield much of the lumber supply. In its own home state it could not compete with the other native trees and shrubs, but under man's care it has replaced the natural forests of remote lands.

On the coast just to the north of San Diego is the Torrey Pines State Park, preserving one of the two remaining groves of this distinct species. The Torrey pine is known for having the smallest natural range of any American pine tree, and anyone can wonder why it exists at all. Off-

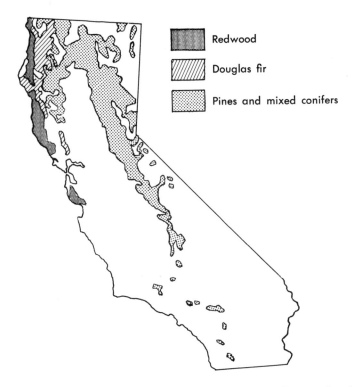

Redwood

Douglas fir

Pines and mixed conifers

FIG. 9. Where California's timber comes from. Except for the redwood region, most the land is in public ownership. Only commercial forest types, suited to timber production, are shown on this map. *Source: U.S. Forest Service*

shore and to the north, the other Torrey pines exist on the island of Santa Rosa and form part of the distinctive flora of the Channel Islands. Also present on these offshore pieces of California are remnants of the peculiar Catalina ironwood, a tree that belongs to a family of plants mostly composed of herbs. It is the only tree belonging to this saxifrage family in North America. Far to the north, on the Mendocino coast, occurs the strange dwarf cypress forming part of a pygmy forest that has developed on relatively sterile sands in an area of peat swamps. The cypresses as a tribe are confined usually to the most sterile habitats. They often occur on areas where the soil is derived from serpentine rock, a rock with an unusual mineral balance that is not capable of supplying adequate nutrition to those plants that are found on normal soils, and supports instead a distinctive flora. Serpentine soils are best represented in the far north of California, on the Oregon side of the Smith River. There one finds a marked contrast between the dense Douglas-fir forest on normal soils, and the open, stunted brush and pine trees of the serpentine.

It would hardly be proper to discuss the trees of California without mentioning the eucalyptus. This antipodean gum tree is now widespread all over California, and gives a strikingly Australian appearance to many landscapes. The eucalyptus came to California in such a way as to bring discredit to many foresters and private businessmen. In a state noted for its various "booms," one of the most strange was the eucalyptus boom of the early 1900's. The first eucalyptus from Australia was planted at San Jose in 1858. More than a decade later a number of these trees were introduced into Southern California and seemed to thrive where other trees did not do well. The common California eucalyptus is the blue gum, *Eucalyptus globulus*. This is a fast-growing hardwood tree that is highly drought-resistant. Since California is deficient in sources of hardwood lumber, it was hoped originally that the Australian gums would produce wood that would find a ready market. The usefulness of the eucalyptus for windbreaks was also stressed by its early promoters. Since eucalyptus oil forms the base for some insect repellents, some of the more wild-eyed promoters of the tree claimed it would rid the state of mosquitoes and cure malaria. The promotion of eucalyptus plantations reached its peak during the first few years of the twentieth century, at which time sober university foresters, and members of the state board of forestry, found themselves in dubious alliance with the most unscrupulous land promoters. The foresters honestly believed that the tree had considerable economic importance in the state's future. The land promoters convinced the gullible that the smartest of investments was one in land planted to eucalyptus seedlings. Blue-gum plantations sprang up everywhere, and land prices boomed. Eucalyptus windbreaks came to surround farms all over California.

The voice of reason began to be heard when the situation in Australia was investigated. It was found that the widely planted blue gum was not one of the more valuable timber trees in its homeland. Indeed, its wood had a marked tendency to warp, shrink, and crack in the process of drying. In Australia, only the largest and oldest trees were commercially useful, and these giants were fast growing only in their early years, long before they were producing worthwhile wood. There were several hundred species of eucalyptus in Australia, but the ones of greatest commercial value there were not adapted to grow rapidly in California. Thus the eucalyptus boom came to an end, and many people were left holding land that could be expected to produce only firewood. Those who had planted windbreaks were better off; the tree was well adapted to that purpose. But in the process the eucalyptus came to California as a permanent resident, and the graceful trees add beauty to many areas. Now, as land prices go up, the Australian trees are again being investigated for possible commercial value on those soils not suited to grow anything of higher economic worth.

However, it was not the peculiarities of California's tree flora that led to the development of the forest industries. Rather it was the vast extent covered by trees of recognized, high commercial value. Logging and lumbering had its beginnings in Spanish times to provide timber for the missions and for Spanish ships. But this was small scale, and involved mostly the use of hand tools, ax and adze. Who first started the commercial lumber business in California has not yet been answered to the satisfaction of all concerned. It is significant, though, that one of the first who engaged in this business, Thomas Larkin, was involved in trespassing difficulties. His employee, William Garner, was ordered off the property of the Amesti Rancho near Monterey where he was accused of illegally cutting down redwoods belonging to someone else. He thus set a precedent that has been followed a bit too often during the long history of the lumber industry.

The cutting of the first giant redwood in California was an epochal event, but it is doubtful that the men who did it had the sophistication to appreciate the accomplishment: small men with small axes hacking away at the base of a tree unlike any other that had ever been cut in America, and finally watching it fall to the ground, smashing smaller trees aside, crushing the undergrowth. When the Roman Empire was still young, the tree had begun to grow. It had stood against the elements during all the centuries when Western civilization was emerging from the ruins of the ancient past. Undoubtedly the men hewed some good timbers from its trunk and built some structure that has long since perished. They could not have known that they were starting the redwood logging industry, one that would eat its way northward through all the giant trees that blanketed the California coastal lands until finally it seemed to threaten the continued existence of the ancient trees.

It was these coastal redwoods that provided the material for the growth of California's forest industries. Located as they were, close to the original centers of population or in areas from which they could be transported by sea in a region that had yet no railroads, it was inevitable that they would be the first to go. In some places they have now been entirely eliminated by the activities of the loggers, followed by settlers who cleared the land. Elsewhere, because they are a tough and resistant species, they have grown back in dense, second-growth stands that will again provide wood in the future. But the old giants will not come back. Man cannot wait a thousand years or more for a tree to grow. Even the most stable lumber company does not plan to operate on a thousand-year cycle of cut and regrowth.

The best viewpoint from which to see the California forest situation today is on the north coast. If you drive north from San Francisco on U.S. Highway 101, you will pass the town of Ukiah, climb a ridge, and come to a wide valley wherein lies Willits. At Willits you have left traditional California. To the north you enter a land that is legally a part of the state, but in most respects still a different world. The Spanish did not settle here; the California climate does not reach here; the vegetation is mostly different. This is the heart of today's timber country—the land of redwood and giant Douglas fir. Here too grows the Sitka spruce, the Port Orford cedar, the western hemlock and the lowland fir. The affinities of the region and its people lie to the northward, to the timber-growing areas of the Pacific Northwest, and historically to New England and Nova Scotia. Untouched by the Spanish tradition, long

cut off from the rest of the state, the region has developed
ways of its own. Once, in disgust with the lack of attention
from the state capital, the northwestern area proposed to
secede from California and join Oregon. The proposal was
in part a joke, but it had merit: the land is more Oregonian
than Californian. Today, when Southern California threatens to dominate the entire state, the old proposal is being
made once more, but with the north now talking of seces-
sion as a separate state. Like the earlier scheme, this one is
also likely to come to nothing.

The northwest coast has long been dominated by the
timber industries. Here has been the last stronghold of the
"lumber baron," the last area where ruthless timber exploitation could be carried out. Nowhere else in California
in recent decades has conservation of the land's resources
been held more in abeyance.

Eureka is the center and seaport of the northwest, and
although it supports only 30,000 inhabitants it is the nearest approximation to a city to be found in Northern California. When only the sea connected the northwest with
San Francisco and civilization, the harbor at Humboldt
Bay, on which Eureka is located, was the key to regional
survival. Later the railroad and the Redwood Highway
came. Now, as four-lane freeways advance northward,
California is at last beginning to claim the area for its own.
The character of the people, the architecture, and even the
landscape is changing. Eureka could be one of the most
beautiful towns in California, backed as it is by redwood-
covered mountains and fronting on a charming setting of
bay, islands, and rolling dunes on the sand spits that enclose the bay. But the town has been built for practicality
and the benefit of business, not for beauty. Its waterfront is
dominated by a slummy area of industrial wasteland and de-

teriorating housing. Throughout the town most residences front only on each other, and fail to look outward to their natural surroundings. Yet, as California towns go, Eureka is one of the more vital and cosmopolitan. It lacks the dreariness and uniformity that characterize most of the centers of population in the northern part of California. It has changed considerably from those past days when Ulysses S. Grant was stationed there, and it was said that "The life of the lonely post was so dreary that, according to legend, he spent much of his time drinking in Ryan's saloon at Eureka. In the end he resigned from the army out of sheer discouragement." * The saloons continue to do business, and the state park officials who occupy Grant's lonely post at Fort Humboldt must often feel like resigning from sheer discouragement, but their reasons are not the same.

Following on World War II, northwestern California was hit by the last great wave of destructive forest exploitation that is likely ever to hit the United States. At this time the region had the greatest reservoir of privately owned, untouched, old-growth Douglas fir to be found in America. The reasons for this were economic. The Douglas fir of Oregon and Washington was once a more extensive resource, and had the advantage of more easy access and better transportation facilities. The large fir lumber companies were established there and commanded the market. California Douglas fir, although of equal quality, was considered essentially worthless in the days before World War II because of its distance from market and from established fir industries. However, the postwar building boom changed that picture. The Oregon and Washington indus-

* *California: A Guide to the Golden State* (New York, Hastings House), Works Progress Administration.

tries had long since stabilized and settled down to a lumber yield based on rates of timber regrowth. They could not meet the sudden demand for lumber. High prices encouraged the get-rich-quick timber operators to move to California.

Local chambers of commerce, always quick to welcome new sources of tax dollars and employment, put no obstacles in the way of the new entrepreneurs. Anyone who could afford a chain saw or a logging truck went into business. Small mills sprang up everywhere, their refuse burners providing a pillar of fire by night and a pillar of smoke by day to guide the way for new immigrants to the region. Local landowners with timber for sale were mostly cattle and sheep men who had paid taxes for years on apparently worthless Douglas-fir land. They were usually only too willing to sell for a minimum price to any buyer, and often quite unaware both of the value of their timber and of the complexities of logging contracts. As time went by, they saw others grow rich on profits from their timber, bought for a fraction of its real value. They saw their lands left in a damaged and sometimes near useless condition when the last of the good logs had been hauled away.

The new Douglas-fir industry, however, moved into an area that had long been a center of commercial logging. With the greatest reserves of redwood timber to be found anywhere, and the availability of ocean transport, the area had an advantage in competition with interior regions of the state. Lumber manufacturing in the Humboldt Bay area began shortly after the Gold Rush, in 1851. At first it supplied timber to the Trinity mines; later it shipped to San Francisco. Between 1851 and 1870 most of the redwoods in the immediate vicinity of Humboldt Bay were cut, and the hills behind Eureka and its sister town of

Arcata were left deforested. After 1870 the region lost some of its economic advantage, as railways brought the pine timber from the Sierra within reach of city markets. The pines, however, were before long to fall under the control of the national forests over broad areas, and thus be removed from easy exploitation. On the coast, however, through some honest land acquisition, seasoned with a considerable sprinkling of land fraud, the redwood country passed from federal to private hands. Redwood was a quality wood that held its market. Giant redwood companies holding great acreages and operating through monster-sized mills at Scotia, Fort Bragg, Samoa, Arcata, and Eureka dominated the coastal industry.

Early methods of redwood logging were rough and ready, but limited in their destructiveness by the absence of machinery. As steam and, later, diesel engines became available, destruction increased. There was no knowledge of forestry practices and no willingness to believe that they could ever be needed. Some of the lands logged over looked as though they could never recover. Fire was used freely, to clear the land before logging, and to destroy the slash afterward. Burned-over slopes were left in a barren, blackened condition. But, surprisingly, they recovered. Some of the worst areas produced excellent stands of second growth. The once-barren slopes around Humboldt Bay are now covered with tall new redwoods, some of them being logged now for a second crop. Through luck the logging and burning treatment that these lands received encouraged sprouting from redwood stumps and roots, so that where one giant tree once grew, a ring of its young descendants now stands.

The redwood industry had left its wild past far behind when the new Douglas-fir boom started. Few redwood lands were available for the new operators to exploit, and so through the boom-and-bust the redwood companies provided a stabilizing influence on the regional economy. It is difficult, however, to assess the damage that the Douglas-fir boom did to the countryside. Bare soil and logging debris were left on the slopes. Stream beds were choked with logging wastes, and their fish populations crippled. When floods hit the region in the winter of 1955–1956, the damage was enormous. The volume of water that poured down the rivers would have been damaging enough. But the rivers also carried soil scoured off the logged-over hillsides, as well as vast quantities of waste logs, downed trees, and slash left behind from logging operations. The damage done must have canceled out any economic gain that the region had made through encouraging or permitting uncontrolled destructive logging. When the fir boom finally came to an end in the middle 1950's, through exhaustion of the supply of timber available to the small mill and the contract logger, the economy of the area suffered a severe setback. For a time it was one of the few parts of California with a declining population. By 1964 it had not fully recovered, and there was little of the easy optimism about growth and prosperity that characterized the early 1950's. In December, 1964, the floods hit once again in still greater force than those of 1955. Once more the valleys were covered by silt from the hillsides. Entire communities vanished almost without a trace. Freeways buckled and bridges were smashed by logs from the sawmill decks, and debris from logged-over hillsides.

The 1950's also brought a major change to the redwood segment of the timber economy. Local control of the lumber industry began to decline. In its place large nation-

The sheer geography of the San Francisco region defies the efforts of those who care nothing for beauty. Despite the spreading freeway network, the glamour of the city remains. *Wide World Photos*

If you drive up the north coast when the mists have not been dispelled by the sunlight, you can build a picture of how things once were and could be again in that region. *Swanlund Photo Lab.*

The famous beaches of California occupy only a small section of the coastline, mostly in the southern and central part of the state. *Photo courtesy of California Division of Beaches and Parks.*

For the most part the California coast is rocky cliff and headland. *Swanlund Photo Lab.*

One of the once remote Channel Islands: Avalon, Santa Catalina.

California countryside. Oak-dotted hills and chaparral-covered mountains of the central coastal region.

Viewed from the east side, the Sierra Nevada seem to form a sheer, impassable mountain wall.

The central Sierra Nevada. Squaw Valley. *California Division of Beaches and Parks.*

The land was shaped by earthquakes, carved by rivers, polished by glaciers. *National Park Service*

Once, golden bands of pronghorns ranged through all of the valley grasslands of California. *James D. Yoakum*

Only in the dark forests of the northwest did the Roosevelt elk survive the first destructive impact of western civilization. *James D. Yoakum*

Coyotes once howled from the headlands where now is the harbor of Los Angeles. *James D. Yoakum*

Waterfowl must now compete for scarce supplies of water against the demands of cities, farms, and industries. *James D. Yoakum*

The old range-livestock industry has gone, and in its place a new one has developed in which quality of wool, lamb, or mutton means far more than numbers of sheep on the range. *Swanlund Photo Lab.*

Efforts to plan for multiple-use, or for complete preservation of forests, are alike defeated by the wildfires that regularly sweep the California countryside during the long, dry summer. *Wide World Photos*

Some measured the growth of redwoods in board feet; others took into account only their spiritual increment. *Charles Yocom*

The redwood giants were not like other trees. Their growth may have started when the Roman Empire was still young. *Swanlund Photo Lab.*

Backed by redwood-covered mountains, fronting on a setting of bay, islands, and dune-swept sandspits, Eureka could be one of California's most beautiful cities. *Swanlund Photo Lab.*

In time, on the cut-over lands, the redwoods grow back. The young trees are our hope for the future, but they can never replace the ancient giants.

Early logging methods were rough and ready in the redwood region. They sowed the seeds for future conflict and misunderstanding. *Swanlund Photo Lab.*

Small lumber mills sprang up everywhere. Their refuse burners provided a pillar of smoke to guide new lumbermen to the region. *Swanlund Photo Lab.*

wide corporations began to come in and buy up the extensive redwood holdings and giant mills. The quiet-spoken organization men of the new corporations displaced the self-made entrepreneurs of an earlier era. Names such as Weyerhaeuser, Simpson, and Georgia-Pacific appeared on the land to displace the familiar local lumber kings. The change brought a greater hope for stability in the industry as the new companies began to pay greater attention to regrowth of cutover lands. A shift toward fuller utilization of forest resources through a more diversified forest industry appeared.

All is not well in the California northwest. Indeed, conflict and misunderstanding are rife. The reasons lie in part with the growth of population elsewhere in the state. Although not matched on the north coast, this growth has brought a demand for new uses of land and a new set of land values that must be applied everywhere. The beginnings of some of the present conflicts, however, lie far in the past. The redwoods of California attracted not only the loggers, who measured their worth in board feet, but other men who looked at the trees in awe and calculated their value in terms of spiritual increment. John Muir came and spent some time in the redwoods. He directed his countrymen to take an interest in the preservation of these forest giants. Many other like-minded people were to follow Muir, and as some of the more flagrant abuses of the early logging days were noticed, a demand for preservation of the giant trees grew. In 1918 the Save-the-Redwoods League was organized, and set out to raise and channel private capital into the acquisition of redwood groves. These were turned over to the state for administration as memorial groves in the California system of state parks. The state was encouraged to acquire still larger blocks of redwood land, to be preserved without cutting for the enjoyment of future generations.

In time the private lumber interests were to view the continued growth of parks and reserves with some concern. To complicate matters, their foresters had not been so successful with obtaining regeneration on cutover redwood lands as had once been hoped. A system of selective logging in which only the larger, older trees are cut and the young ones allowed to continue growth had been instituted. This left the land in reasonably good condition, but unfortunately did not result in the expected reproduction. Seedlings did not become established in sufficient numbers, nor was stump-sprouting adequate for replacement. Windstorms caused damage in the opened redwood stands and interfered greatly with management plans. It was therefore decided to try clear-cutting, removal of all the trees, accompanied by a maximum soil disturbance. It was hoped that the bare, unshaded mineral soil, exposed in this process, would provide a better site for the growth of seedlings. This program, however, creates lands that look as though they had been subjected to heavy bombardment and artillery shelling over a period of years. They are a shocking contrast to the old-growth stands, and an obvious source of soil loss and watershed disturbance. Their appearance alone has brought new supporters to the ranks of those who want to preserve a maximum area of old-growth redwood, and these people in turn cause cold chills among the other groups whose income depends upon the maintenance of a lively redwood logging industry.

It is always dangerous to have a single industry dominate the economy of a region. When most of the employment is offered by the forest industries, when most of the money is brought into the region by these industries, when most subsidiary businesses depend for their prosperity upon the continued production of forest products, it is difficult for the people of the region to be objective or take a broad view. Each public issue is viewed, not on its overall merits, but on its effect upon the local economy, meaning the timber industries. In 1964 a clear demonstration of this was provided when various proposals for a new freeway were being considered. There were, basically, three possible routes for this freeway. One was to follow the existing highway through the middle of one of the major redwood state parks, Prairie Creek. Since the park was formed after the existing highway was built, it has been a necessary fact of life in the park's management. However, lining the present highway are most of the major memorial groves of redwoods, presented to the state of California through private acquisition and donation. Widening the two-lane highway into a four-lane freeway would necessarily destroy the heart of these memorial groves. A second proposal was to build the highway along the west side of the state park, below the spectacular Gold Bluffs where the forested land comes to meet the sea. Below these sheer cliffs is an attractive wild beach, one of the few extensive areas of wild beach left in California. Though it is accessible only by a winding country road, it is well known to all who enjoy wild scenery. It provides a home and feeding ground for a large herd of Roosevelt elk, along with many other wild animals. Obviously, if a freeway were built on the beach it would no longer be a wild place and its aesthetic and recreational value would be reduced to the same level as the many miles of highway-fringed beaches that are to be found south of the state park.

A final alternative route for the freeway was along a

ridge lying east of the state park. This would take it through land controlled by lumber companies, most of which had been logged over in the past. No wild country, and few giant redwoods, would be destroyed by this route, although it would provide a scenic view out over the park to the ocean. Anyone interested in state parks, old redwoods, wildlife, or wild beaches was immediately attracted by the third, ridge, route for the highway. However, this route would cost more money, remove more private land from the county tax rolls, and would provide grades on the highway that would slow down logging and lumber trucks. When the issue came to a public hearing, there was little doubt of the outcome. Almost without exception the local Chambers of Commerce, most of the county supervisors and other official spokesmen, the local newspapers, radio and television stations, and, naturally enough, the lumber industry, opposed the ridge route. Many absurd arguments were advanced in apparent sincerity about the benefits that would accrue from opening up the wild beach to the public by building a freeway over it, or the advantages that would accrue to the region by cutting the heart out of the redwood state park. Basically all were opposed to any move that would interfere in the slightest way with the local lumber-based economy, regardless of any broader issues of importance to the state and the nation. A similar opposition has appeared on every other issue of public importance: prevention of air pollution through elimination of mill refuse burners or control over the proposed pulp mills; prevention of damage to stream sides and water resources by logging; expansion of public parks and recreation areas. Nothing is approved that will interfere with or upset those who control the forest industries.

It is easy to criticize the lumber industry, and at times

it is richly deserving of criticism. Yet it must be pointed out, in fairness, that it receives much unwarranted blame. The region is one of the most highly productive timber-growing areas in the world, and even the most ardent conservationist uses wood and paper. It is just as important to the welfare of the nation to keep a healthy, productive forest industry working in this region as it is to set aside some parts of the area in inviolate preserves. Important though parks and wilderness areas may be, no country can survive solely on these alone. The economy of the nation cannot be based on recreation. We do not create wealth by viewing each other's scenic resources. Somebody has to cut wood.

In mid-1964 the conflict between the northwest timber industries and those who favor parks and recreation was brought into still sharper focus when the National Park Service issued its proposals for a new Redwood National Park. This park, along with proposed additions to the state park system, would involve the purchase of some 50,000 acres of land, including approximately 25,000 acres of virgin growth, at a maximum; or roughly 30,000 acres of land and 15,000 acres of virgin redwood, at a minimum. It would involve the virtual elimination of the entire holdings of the Arcata Redwood Company, one of the region's largest. Naturally enough the plan met the complete opposition of the lumber companies, business interests, Chambers of Commerce, press and television, and local governmental bodies of northwestern California.

There should be some middle ground between forest preservationists and forest industries. That it is difficult to find is in part the industry's fault. There is much talk by industry representatives about sustained-yield forest production, the stability of the timber industries, and their long-run contribution to the economy of the country. Yet the timber stands appear to be melting away, and the second-growth stands that will support the economy when the old growth is gone are difficult to find. The National Park Service states that of 2,000,000 acres of original redwood forest, approximately 750,000 acres of old growth remain, of which 300,000 are untouched virgin growth. Only 50,000 acres are preserved in state parks. There are reported to be some 16 billion board feet of old-growth redwood timber available for use, but the present rate of cut is in the neighborhood of a billion board feet a year. Does this mean that the industry will cut back sharply after sixteen years, when it must shift to a second-growth supply? Does this in turn mean a marked reduction in employment and a drastic effect on the local economy? If industry does not propose to cut back, where are the second-growth stands that will support it? If it does propose to cut back, it is hardly fair to the local population to pretend that such a cutback will not occur. National parks are meant to last forever, but they can only be set aside now. Good forestry practices, and a conservative program for sustained yield forest production, can also mean a forest economy that will last forever, but the evidence that these are truly in effect must be advanced now.

Away from the north coast most of the forests of California are now national forests, under the management of the United States Forest Service. The California region includes eighteen national forests that cover nearly one-fifth of the land area of the state. These are dedicated to the principle of multiple use, meaning that each forest will be managed not for the benefit of one industry or group, but for maximum benefits to all the people. Although production of timber crops is recognized as a major use of

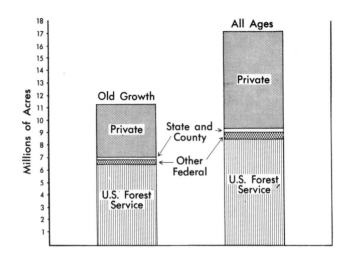

FIG. 10. Private timberlands in California were cut over first, leaving the national forests in reserve. Today most of California's old-growth commercial forest is under Forest Service management. This chart shows the acreage of commercial forest in various ownerships. *Source: U.S. Forest Service, 1954*

the forests, it is nowhere given sole consideration. Protection of soil and watershed is always a first priority. The forest must also meet demands for recreation, provide a home for wildlife, provide grazing for domestic animals and supply any other possible benefits to the people of the nation. The local economy of the region in which the forest is located is given special consideration but not to an extent that would damage the national interest. All resources in the forest that are cropped or harvested are managed on the principle of sustained yield, in which rates of harvest are balanced against rates of growth, so that the forests will remain permanently productive of timber, forage, and wildlife. These objectives are all noble, and could they be followed in practice they would provide for a system of land management above criticism. The rub comes in putting the ideal into practical operation.

For most of the years that they have existed, the California national forests have been in practice, but not in principle, forest preserves. The Forest Service has acted as custodian for government timber, while the lumber industries were concerned with cutting over the privately owned lands. Only with the private timber supply fully exploited has there been a great demand for government wood. Consequently the Forest Service has been mainly in the business of protecting the woods from fire, or attempting to quell outbreaks of forest diseases or insect pests. Only small areas were logged, and these could readily be fitted into the sustained-use scheme. Now, however, there is a steady, incessant pressure for more and more government timber. The national forests have been asked to supply the full sustained yield that they have promised. But they are asked to supply this while still protecting the basic resources of soil and water, and meeting public needs for recreation, grazing, and wildlife management.

If all of the necessary knowledge and techniques for good land management were available, the forest officer would still have a difficult task in reconciling the various public demands for use of the national forests. But much of the basic knowledge about the cutting and production of timber crops is not available. The relationship of logging to other uses of the land is a subject only partially investigated. Furthermore the knowledge cannot be acquired without slow trial-and-error experiment. Consequently, although the forest ranger may feel that he should proceed slowly and with caution in making timber available for cutting, he is under steady pressure to open up more land. Although he may feel that current logging practices are damaging, he is under pressure to remove restrictions rather than increase them. Since the logger has a single purpose in mind—the making of maximum profit from the sale of forest products—he is not readily sidetracked or confused. The forest administrator, however, does not have the factual knowledge needed for the decisions he must make.

It is not possible today to say whether or not the national forests are being properly managed. We can find this answer only in the future. There is a widespread feeling among foresters that the pace is too fast and that the control is not sufficient, and this uneasiness is transferred to the visiting public. The forest camper, hunter, or tourist is appalled at the appearance of some cutover lands, at obvious losses of recreational value, at possible damage to soil or watershed. He is often not easily persuaded that the best possible methods are being used. But timber is a slow-growing crop, and the establishment of seedlings on cutover lands is an uncertain business. We have not had the centuries of experience with logging and regrowth available to the foresters of Europe, and our conditions are different from theirs. It may take fifty years or more to test our present methods. Meanwhile the optimists will hope and the pesimists despair.

The forests of California, despite a century of logging, destructive wild fires, forest insects, and fungus diseases, are still green. The state has one of the largest areas of old-growth virgin forest that remain in the United States, approximately 10,000,000 acres. This represents more than half of the total area of commercial timber land. Yet the outlook is not entirely encouraging. The most recent general survey of the forest situation indicated that where the annual growth was close to 600,000,000 cubic feet of wood per year, the annual loss from all causes, including timber harvest, was more than twice that amount. A drain of perhaps 700,000,000 cubic feet per year was being removed from forest capital. The annual cut of saw timber, measured in board feet, was nearly 6,000,000,000. Almost all this was being taken from the old-growth stands of timber, which therefore represented a supply that could last no more than fifty years. However, since cutting means replacement of slow-growing old trees with fast-growing young trees, rates of growth and loss would tend to come into balance over a period of time, as long as proper attention is given to encouraging reseeding of the cutover lands. The situation on private lands is more critical than on public, and is revealed by a survey carried out in Humboldt County. This states:

"Today, more than 200 manufacturing plants are using the remaining old-growth timber at a rate of about 1¼ billion board feet per year. And Humboldt County is on the crest of a wave of industrial expansion, having tripled its annual lumber production during the past eight years. But only 18 billion feet of timber remain on the tax rolls. Loggers have had to reach out to increasingly remote tracts for current cutting. Timber has become scarcer and much more costly. And part of the cutover land appears to support little new timber growth."

This report was issued ten years ago. Now the effects have been fully felt, and government rather than private timber is expected to take up the slack.

The Forest Service, like other public agencies, is subjected to severe degrees of pressure from special-interest groups. Thus, during the period immediately after World War II, several associations of stockmen set out to wrest control over grazing in national forests from the federal government, with the view to turning the grazing lands over to the state, or ultimately to private ownership. Through the influence of congressional representatives from the western grazing states, a series of public hearings was conducted throughout the West to bring pressure to bear to accomplish this end. Many of the hearings were disgracefully conducted, the audience packed with stockmen for the purpose of ridiculing and browbeating Forest Service officers. Fortunately, these produced repercussions when the public realized what was going on. The stockmen and their congressmen were forced into full retreat. But such efforts never cease entirely. The private interests who wish to speed up rates of timber harvest and ease up on restrictions governing logging seldom put on such a spectacular Wild West show as that produced by the cowboys, but their pressure can be equally enervating to the morale of the public service. The general public can ask reassurance that the national interest is not being damaged through the increasing rate of timber harvest. But to be sure that the public land is properly cared for, they must be as steady and unwavering in their concern as the special-interest groups are persistent in their pressures.

There are many who doubt that the public has sufficient control over the activities of private lumber companies operating on private lands. The consequences of inadequate control have been seen particularly where contract loggers have operated on lands that are owned by others. Efforts at achieving control have had a long history in the state legislature, and for many decades met with no success. A simple approach to the problem was advanced by an Assemblyman Wemple in 1925 with a bill that stated: "Any person who shall wantonly, wastefully, or unnecessarily cut or destroy trees or vegetation necessary for the protec-

tion of watersheds of the state is guilty of a misdemeanor."
Not unexpectedly, the bill failed to pass. Had it done so,
the courts might still be hearing arguments over the meaning of "wanton" "wasteful," and "unnecessary." However,
some control was needed. In 1945 a Forest Practices Act
was passed that supposedly provided for "forest practices
which will promote maximum sustained productivity of
the forest lands of California." Unfortunately, the bill had
no provision for enforcement, and left the forest practices
to be determined by the timber operators of each region,
subject to the approval of the State Board of Forestry. Its
ineffectiveness was demonstrated in the decade that followed its passage. In 1957 an effort was made to put some
teeth into the law by requiring all timber operators to obtain a permit to operate, with appropriate penalties for
failure to do so. Those who failed to comply with the
forest-practice rules in effect in their region could have
their permits to operate revoked. However, even in this
revised form major emphasis was placed on self-regulation
by the forest industries, and the penalties for failure to
conform were small by comparison with the profits to be
gained.

It is difficult to legislate proper management of any
living natural resource. We are still groping for the knowledge of ecology necessary before effective management
can be formulated. We cannot suspend activities until the
knowledge is available, for we must continue to eat, and
build houses. The best hope is through public encouragement of those industries and operators that show a public-
spirited approach to the problems of resource management
and use, and a clear dedication to conservation principles
among the custodians of the public lands.

SIX

SAVING THE
PIECES

Are we no longer capable of respecting nature,
or defending a living beauty that has no earn-
ing power, no utility, no object except to let
itself be seen from time to time? Liberty, too,
is a natural splendor on its way to becoming
extinct.   —ROMAIN GARY *

IN 1851 the Indians were acting up in the country southeast of Stockton. A particularly troublesome band, working
out of the Sierra, refused to respect any authority other
than that of its own chief, Tenaya. To teach them a lesson
and set them in their proper place, an armed party under
the leadership of Major James Savage set forth in pursuit. Through the foothills and into the mountains they
followed the trail of the Indians, seeking the hiding place
from which they had raided with previous impunity. In
the party was L. H. Bunnell, who left us with a record of
his experience when, on March 21, they suddenly saw
before them the hiding place, the secret valley, of the
Yosemite Indians:

* *The Roots of Heaven.*

"The immensity of rock I had seen in my vision on the Old Bear Valley trail was here presented to my astonished gaze. . . . None but those who have visited this wonderful valley can even imagine the feelings with which I looked upon the view that was there presented. The grandeur of the scene was but softened by the haze that hung over the valley—light as gossamer—and by the clouds which partially dimmed the higher cliffs and mountains. An exalted sensation seemed to fill my whole being, and I found my eyes in tears with emotion." *

Eighty-two years had passed since the Spanish colonists arrived in California. That Yosemite had remained undiscovered for so long seems remarkable. But the old *Californios* in their lotos land were not pushed by the same restless drives that had sent their forebears into all the far corners of Latin America. Some years before Savage's arrival in Yosemite, the Walker party had crossed the Sierra and stood not far from the rim of the great valley, but they did not see it, and went on to the west. So it remained for Tenaya's band to reveal their own stronghold.

Once discovered, the ice-carved wonderland of Yosemite could not remain undisturbed. Word spread, and others came to look, to seek for gold, to graze livestock, and some finally to stay. Before long, those who cared for the natural grandeur of the place became concerned with what might happen to it were it left open to the hydraulic miner and the timber cutter. Telling tales of its wonders in the halls of Washington, they prevailed upon Congress in 1864 to pass an Act for its preservation. Under the terms of the Act the Yosemite Valley and the nearby Mariposa Grove of giant sequoias were set aside as a park. Since no

* From Valeska Bari, *The Course of Empire* (New York, Coward-McCann, 1931).

federal agency was on hand to administer it, the park was turned over to the State of California to become the first state park in the nation. Thus was the first step taken toward the preservation of the unique, the spectacular, and later the merely representative pieces of wild California. During the 1860's and 1870's there was no drive toward the preservation of wilderness. Most of the West was far too wild for comfort, and the main interest was in preserving American settlers and the homes, farms, and villages that they were trying to establish. People, not wild lands, were scarce and precious. But the rate at which things changed, even in those days, could be frightening. In California the miners showed that they could quickly ruin any land in their insatiable quest for gold. Hydraulic mining washed away mountains and sent their pieces down the streams to silt up the valleys. Timber for mines and mining towns was obtained by destroying the nearest forest. Wildlife was decimated for meat and leather. By 1862 William Brewer was writing with disgust of this devastation, and blaming the flood damage of 1861–1862 on the activities of miners. Back east, the picture was even more clear. There the influence of unrestrained exploitation of the land was becoming too much in evidence in the eighties and nineties. The feeling for conservation and for preservation of America's natural beauty and wildlife was becoming strong. In 1890 its effects were felt in California. A large stretch of the Sierra Nevada was permanently withdrawn from private use. Three national parks, Yosemite, including all of the hinterland surrounding Yosemite Valley; General Grant, enclosing the largest grove of giant sequoias; and Sequoia, including a spectacular area in the southern Sierra, were created. The parks were intended to preserve the wild scenery, the vegetation, and the animal life of the area.

Grazing, hunting, logging, and other forms of destructive use were prohibited. To provide protection the United States Army was moved in and given charge of the park administration.

The army had an interesting job, because by 1890 many people had begun to feel that they had some vested right in the resources now set aside in national parks. Most difficult to control were the stockmen. John Muir had watched their activities in the days before the park was created, and wrote of meadows ground into dust, of hillsides left barren and terraced with the trails of sheep. Trespass of livestock across the new park boundaries went on. The owners claimed an inability to control the movements of their animals. However, when an enterprising military commander decided to release trespassing livestock on the opposite side of the park from that on which they were captured, a distance of thirty or more miles, the stockmen suddenly found that they could, after all, keep their animals out of the new parks.

John Muir wrote: "The best service in forest protection —almost the only efficient service—is that rendered by the military. For many years they have guarded the great Yellowstone Park, and now they are guarding the Yosemite. They have found it a desert as far as underbrush grass and flowers were concerned, but in two years the skin of the mountains is healthy again. Blessings on Uncle Sam's soldiers. They have done the job well, and every pine tree is waving its arms for joy." *

The story of landownership in California is an interesting if confusing tale. Presumably the land originally belonged to the Indians, but this was one claim that was ignored by common consent of the white invaders. The

* *John of the Mountains.*

Spanish exercised their claim over part of the land for the dual motive of protecting the Spanish investment in the Western Hemisphere and of saving the souls of the California Indians. Therefore the Spanish settlements were to feature a *presidio*, or military base, and a mission, or religious base. Springing up as an adjunct to either was the *pueblo*, or town, representing a secular, nonmilitary authority. The missions became the principal landholding institution in Spanish California. Mission farms, manned by the captive Christianized Indians, spread over the fertile valley soils, while the mission livestock grazed over great tracts of grazing land. By the time that the twenty-first, and last, mission was established, in 1823 at Sonoma, the Franciscan missions effectively controlled one-sixth of the total land in California, and most of central and south-coastal California.

The area under control of pueblos and presidios remained small while the Spanish held sway, and only a few private individuals held claim to land outside the military or town boundary. However, in 1821, the fire started by Simón Bolívar in South America had spread to and destroyed the rule of Spain in Mexico. Mexico became independent, and the Spanish Californians pledged their allegiance to Mexico, not Spain, in 1822. With this new independence came a wave of revolt against the authority of the missions, until finally, in 1833, an Act of the Mexican Congress removed the missions from Franciscan control, secularized them, and essentially stripped them of their lands and labor. For many parts of the state this meant ruin and collapse. The once-prosperous missions fell into decay; the pueblos that had grown around them were deserted, and an atmosphere of gloom prevailed. This was noted by William Brewer even as late as 1861. Visiting the once-thriving community of Santa Barbara, he wrote:

"It was with a feeling of much sadness that I rode through the old town. Here were whole streets of buildings, built of *adobes,* their roofs gone, their walls tumbling, squirrels burrowing in them—all now desolate, ruined, deserted. Grass grows in the old streets and cattle feed in the gardens. Extensive yards (*corrals*) built with stone walls, high and solid, stand without cattle. The old threshing floor is ruined, the weeds growing over its old pavement. The palm trees are dead, and the olive and fig trees are dilapidated and broken." *

With the decline of the missions, a new era of land-ownership began, brought about by the Mexican land-grant system. Small plots and farms were taken up, but most particularly the day of the big *rancho* owned by a wealthy *ranchero* had arrived. Many individuals obtained title to land within the former mission area; a title not recognized by the church. Since neither title nor boundary of a land grant was always clearly defined, a legal problem was inherited when California became a part of the United States. For many years the courts wrestled with the question of who owned what. Great confusion resulted in some areas. North of San Francisco Bay where the city of Vallejo now stands, the entire area was at one time a land grant. This grant, in time, was sold to various individuals who converted it into farms and townships. Two towns, Vallejo and Benecia, grew up on it, with residences and business establishments. Then, fourteen years after the initial sale, the courts decided that the original land grant was invalid and that the entire area, occupied or not, was to be classified as "public land, open for settlement." The struggle that fol-

* *Up and Down California in 1860–1864.*

lowed between established settler and newly arrived squatter became intense. William Brewer, who recorded this incident in 1862, also noted how nearly the whole of Marin County was owned by thirty individuals, the holders of the original Mexican grants. Thus, he pointed out, of the 330,000 acres in the county, only 2,000 were public land open to settlement. Brewer's regret that this was impeding the development of the county seems ironical enough today.

During Spanish and Mexican rule the boundaries of California were never clearly defined. The Spanish were coast-oriented, and had little interest in the interior or northern portion of the state. This was essentially Indian land, claimed at the time by no one else. With the coming of statehood, however, all of California's land came under some form of ownership. Those land grants that were legally recognized continued as private lands. Many were sold, subsequently, but a few remained essentially unchanged down through the years, small islands of near permanency in a general sea of change. The missions themselves were able to establish legal claim to only 40,000 acres of ranching land outside the actual mission grounds. Most of the state became public domain, under the ownership of the federal government and the jurisdiction of the General Land Office.

The practice of the federal government during the early history of the American West was to dispose of public land as rapidly as possible. Homesteading was encouraged, particularly after the passage of the Homestead Act of 1862. Much of the more productive land in the state went over to private ownership at that time, whereas the more remote or less fertile lands remained under government control. California, perhaps more than most places, has been afflicted since early times with land speculators. Brewer decried this practice in 1862, writing: "Sausalito is a place of half a dozen houses, once 'destined' to be a great town; $150,000 lost there—city laid out, corner lots sold at enormous prices; 'water fronts' still higher—for a big city was bound to grow up there, and then these lots would be worth money. The old California story—everybody *bought land* to rise in value, but no one *built*, no city grew there. Half a dozen huts and shanties mark the place, and 'corner lots' and 'water fronts' are alike valueless. This was on the same ranch with 'Lime Point,' where $400,000 was asked of Uncle Sam for a spot of land worth $100 at the highest figure, to build a fort on, but never bought." * Another writer has described what happened in Los Angeles, a particularly fertile ground for real-estate speculation up to this day. Following the completion of the railroad to the East in 1885: "Within little more than two years the population swelled from 12,000 to 50,000. Many swept in on the tidal wave were homeseekers, but most came to make a fortune in real estate, and to make it quick. At first the little town scarcely knew what was happening. Buildings went up overnight. Land speculation reached fantastic proportions. Lots around the Plaza sold at $1,000 a front foot; subdivisions were laid out from Santa Monica to San Bernardino, a distance of 70 miles; promoters paid cash in advance for full-page advertisements to spur the dilatory: . . . Money talked, and talked loudly, until 1887 when the banks suddenly refused to loan on real estate except at pre-boom value. The bubble burst, scores of paper 'millionaires' found themselves penniless. Salvaging what they could, people fled the city at the rate of 3,000 a month." †

* *Ibid.*
† *California: A Guide to the Golden State.*

In California's early history government ownership of land did not imply government protection for the land. Livestock were grazed, timber was cut, wildlife was shot, mines were claimed, and the users of the public land felt that through this activity they had established some sort of permanent claim to the products of the federal land, while accepting none of the responsibility of ownership. Even private land was not exempt from exploitation by others, as witnessed by the legal provision for the grazing of livestock on any lands not actually fenced. Even after the responsibility for livestock trespass was placed on the shoulder of the stockmen, the public attitude toward private lands remained ambiguous. People today assume a right to hunting, fishing, camping, or picnicking, and are prone to ignore fences. Only a house or garden, or an intensively farmed field, is truly private in the public regard. If land looks wild, some element of public claim to it always remains.

Today, well over a century since California became a state, 45,000,000 acres of the 100,000,000 within the boundary of California are still federal land. This does no longer mean, as it once did, that these lands are not wanted by private individuals. Instead it signifies the importance of the process, which began with Yosemite, of removing permanently from private claim those lands in which the general public has a compelling interest. The 45,000,000 federal acres are broken up under many federal jurisdictions, from parks to military lands. Nearly all of it, however, is now watched over and managed, permanently withdrawn from sale or disposal, reserved for public use.

The establishment in the Sierra Nevada of three national parks marked the beginnings of the National Park system of California. In 1908 another step was taken when two areas, a small redwood grove in Marin County, and the rocky peaks of the Pinnacles, south of Hollister, were set aside as national monuments. The former was named for the man who had been leading the fight for saving wild California in established national parks, John Muir. Beginning in 1892, those who were using public land for their own purposes received another kind of setback when, in the mountains above Los Angeles, the San Gabriel Forest Reserve was created. This, the first of California's national forests, was intended to protect the vital watershed from which the water supply of Los Angeles was obtained. It was soon joined by other major additions, the Sierra, south of Yosemite Park, and the Trabuco Canyon and San Bernardino areas, vital Southern California watersheds. During following years, and particularly during the presidency of Theodore Roosevelt, the national-forest system of California was largely filled out. Unlike the parks, the national forests were not withdrawn from commercial use; but such use was regulated. The first rangers who came west to administer the national forests had a difficult job convincing the local people that the era of free wood and grazing had come to an end. To this date the Forest Service has not been entirely successful in establishing this idea.

With the establishment of national forests and parks, much of California public land was protected. The remainder, however, continued open to abuse, and received this in full measure until the 1930's. Under the administration of Franklin Roosevelt, a new wave of interest in conservation brought the passage of the Taylor Grazing Act, establishing some degree of control over livestock use of the public domain. Finally, in 1946, when the Bureau of Land Management was created in the Department of the

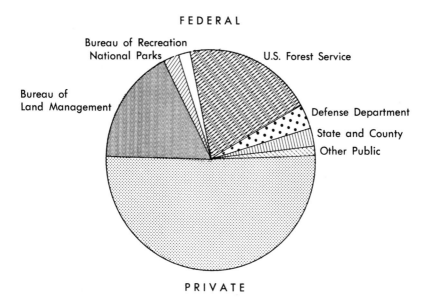

FEDERAL

Bureau of Recreation
National Parks

U.S. Forest Service

Bureau of
Land Management

Defense Department

State and County

Other Public

PRIVATE

California Landownership

FIG. 11. Nearly half of California's land is still in federal ownership. The Forest Service and Bureau of Land Management are responsible for the protection and management of more than one-third of the land in the state.

Interior, the last of the public land was brought under some degree of management.

Through all of this the original claimants to the land, the California Indians, were pushed from place to place; traded, cheated, or robbed of their heritage, they were finally herded into a few large reservations and a number of smaller *rancherías*. In 1850 treaties were signed between the United States Government and the various Indian tribes. In return for recognizing United States sovereignty and the cession of their land rights, the Indians were left with some 7,500,000 acres they could call their own, and were promised various kinds of federal assistance. The United States Congress, at that time, was in no mood for treating with Indians, and failed to ratify the treaties. In subsequent years the Indians were robbed of some 7,000,-000 acres of their legal land and crowded into what was left. It was not until 1963 that the courts finally recognized the legal claims of the Indians and granted them a sum of $27,000,000 in payment for their land. Since this constituted a recognition of the rights of the Indians, some have suggested that the Indians turn down the money and take back their land. Fortunately, this has not been taken seriously, or an unfortunate precedent might be set, recalling that Alaska was purchased from the Russians for a much lower price, and that Manhattan Island, after all, went on the block for $24 and a few trifles.

The drive to save bits and pieces of California from the exploiter did not halt with the establishment of the first national parks and monuments, or with the setting aside of forest reserves. It would be tedious to catalogue every addition to the list, but some are worth noting. The establishment of the National Park Service in 1916 removed the national parks from military guardianship and substituted that of professional park rangers. In the same year Lassen Volcanic National Park was added to the California system, preserving the great area of volcanoes and lava flows surrounding Mount Lassen. Nine years later the Lava Beds National Monument was created, bringing under protection another section of the volcanic wonderland that was once the scene of the Modoc Indian War. In the 1930's two huge national monuments, totaling 2,500,000 acres, were staked out in the desert; Death Valley, preserving the lowest, hottest, and one of the most scenic places in the nation; and Joshua Tree, protecting the strange yuccas for which it was named, and a broad area of relatively undisturbed desert vegetation. In the same decade the unique qualities of California's neglected Channel Islands were recognized with the establishment of the small national monument covering Santa Barbara and Anacapa islands, breeding grounds for sea birds, sea lions, and elephant seals. In 1940 a long intramural battle between the departments of Agriculture and the Interior led to the Kings Canyon area, rivaling the Yosemite in beauty and equally beloved by John Muir, being established as a national park instead of remaining a national forest. Along with the giant sequoias of General Grant, it became the Kings Canyon National Park.

But the National Park Service was not alone in offering protection to wild, remote, and scenic lands. The United States Forest Service, during the 1920's, through the prompting of such men as Aldo Leopold and Robert Marshall, had recognized the importance of wilderness preservation. The realization that some sections of national forest land could serve their highest use and contribute more to the national welfare by remaining wild led to the establishment within the national forests of Wilderness Areas and Wild Areas. These areas were protected from road development, timber cutting, and other uses that would destroy the primitive scene. Unlike the national parks, they could be used for limited grazing and public hunting, but were not to be developed for these purposes. The first Wilderness Area was established in 1924 in the Gila region of Arizona. In California, many such areas were established in the 1930's. Notable among them, the most spectacular section of the Coast Ranges, the high Yolla Bolly Mountain region, was set aside; the jagged peaks and deep canyons between the Salmon and Trinity rivers in the Klamath

Mountains, and an area along the spine of the High Sierra in the Inyo, Sierra, and Sequoia national forests. The three totaled 822,000 acres. In addition, some fourteen other areas, too small to be called wilderness, were designated as Wild Areas and were afforded essentially the same degree of protection. These, totaling nearly 600,000 acres, were distributed from San Diego County in the south to the Warner Mountains in the northeast. They included representative sections of almost every kind of vegetation and terrain broadly represented in the national forest system.

The California state government entered into the preservation of natural areas early when it assumed charge of Yosemite Valley during the 1860's. The original State Park Commission was politically oriented, and aroused the ire of conservationists, who fought hard to have Yosemite Valley placed under federal control. In 1927, however, the California Division of Beaches and Parks was established and charged with the administration of those areas set aside for recreational purposes, historical monuments, or for the preservation of natural scenery and vegetation. Modeled largely on the National Park Service, this division has done an admirable job. By the early 1950's more than 100 areas had been established, from public beaches of a few acres in size on the crowded coastline of Southern California to the Borego-Anza Desert Park that protects 460,000 acres of the old Colorado Desert of San Diego County. Included under the protection of the state park system are more than 75,000 acres of coastal redwood forest.

In the 1960's the realization that California's seacoast was disappearing under private development at a rate that boded ill for the future brought a demand that some additional portion of it be saved. Through congressional action the coast of Marin County, including the historic site on

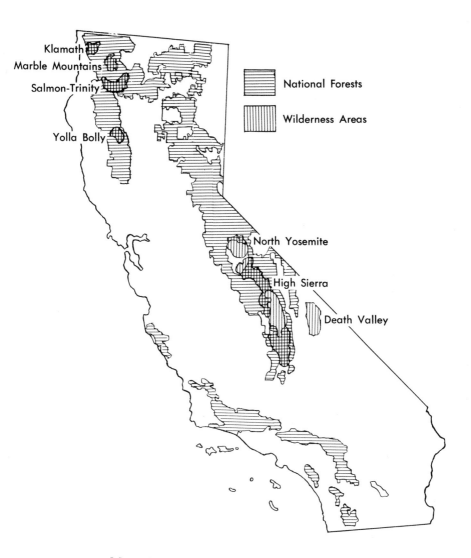

FIG. 12. More than any other single agency, the Forest Service is responsible for California's wild land. Not only do the national forests contain most of the remaining old-growth commercial timberland; they also include most of the remaining wilderness. *Source: Outdoor Recreation Resources Review Commission*

Point Reyes where Francis Drake first set foot on California, was established as the Point Reyes National Seashore, under National Park Service protection. Always the battle for protection of the natural scene has been led by private groups and individuals. The senior group, founded through the efforts of John Muir in 1892, was the Sierra Club. Since that time this club has been active in every conservation battle, from Hetch Hetchy to Bodega Head. They have fought valiantly for the preservation of wild country, have served as watchdogs over government agencies charged with conservation, and have done a splendid job of bringing to the public a greater appreciation of the values to be found in nature. The Audubon Society, though primarily concerned with the preservation of bird life, has also joined in the general struggle for effective conservation of the land. The Wilderness Society and National Parks Association have played active roles. More recently a different approach has been tried by the Nature Conservancy. This group has carried out an inventory of imperiled areas of unusual scientific value, and has raised funds for their purchase. This organization has found that despite the systems of parks and wilderness preserves, many of the original types of vegetation in California were completely unprotected. They have sought out tracts of natural prairie, marshes, bogs, sand dunes, and other bits of vanishing wild land. A major accomplishment has been the acquisition and protection of a large acreage of virgin Douglas-fir forest.

Unfortunately, there is more to preserving wild country and natural vegetation than having it designated as such on a map. This may be adequate for mountains and rocks, but living things are not static. The tree in the national park grows, becomes old, and dies. Park boundaries do not save it forever. Animal populations will come and go despite legislation. All creatures follow dynamic laws of natural succession unless we interfere actively. In setting aside parks we have not always been clear about our purposes, and have seldom begun to envision the problems involved. In the Sierra forests are extensive stands of ponderosa pine. These originally were open forests, the trees separated by an understory of grass, creeping shrubs, or various herbs. Many believe that the forests were kept open by periodic fires. The issue is not clear, but the tree trunks of older trees show a history of past occurrence of fire, predating the white man's appearance. Despite this, one of the first things that we have done in the national parks and forests was to exclude fire. To the extent that we have been successful in this purpose, we have removed one of the natural forces that may have maintained the forest. Some complain that formerly open stands of pine are growing up with thick underbrush and pine reproduction. Such stands, when a fire does strike, burn hotly and are completely destroyed. Under more open conditions a ground fire could go through without damaging the trees. But in some places the parks or forests have now been protected for seventy or more years. Everywhere there is some accumulation of litter. The conditions that existed at a time when light burning would do no damage no longer exist. Start a fire now and you lose a forest. Keep fire out and the forest continues to change, perhaps into something you do not want.

In the national parks, initially, protection was offered to all kinds of wildlife, except predatory animals. Until the late 1930's, predatory-animal control was a regular national-park practice intended to afford protection to game animals. Now the wolves and grizzlies are gone. The mountain lion, whose beat may carry him around an area fifty miles in diameter, is almost certain to leave the park and become vulnerable to trappers or hunters outside. The coyote and bobcat also, with numbers trimmed down along the edges of the parks, cannot achieve a natural abundance inside. Without adequate controls, some kinds of game animals, deer and elk in particular, have increased to exceedingly high densities. Overabundant herds threaten destruction of natural vegetation, and themselves fall victim of malnutrition or disease.

In 1962 the Secretary of the Interior, Stewart Udall, appointed a committee headed by A. Starker Leopold to investigate this problem. By this time a vociferous demand was being heard from the sportsmen's clubs and various state fish-and-game departments, demanding that the parks be thrown open to public hunting. After much consideration and inspection of the problem areas, the committee decided against public hunting within the national parks. They recommended, however, that the National Park Service face up to the necessity of managing both vegetation and animal life, instead of proceeding in hope that both would take care of themselves if given sufficient protection. It was recommended that overabundant herds of deer and elk be reduced, not by the public, but by the Park Service or others designated by them for this purpose. Objections to public hunting included both doubt as to its efficiency and the danger of setting a precedent for other groups that wished special rights within the parks.

In 1963 a campaign was carried out in Yosemite National Park against an insect that was destroying the extensive forests of lodgepole pine. Large areas were sprayed with malathion, an effective insecticide. Almost immediately there was a public outcry from those who feared the possible side effects upon bird and other animal life. Yet the Park Service was caught in another dilemma of protection. Should protection include damaging insects, even when these were destroying trees? Should nature really be allowed to "take its course"? Would the trees have been damaged if controlled burning had been carried out as part of the park management program?

There are those who fear the heavy hand of management applied to wilderness and park areas, where the objective is to preserve the wild and primitive. Their fears are solidly based. Early in Yosemite history one caretaker decided that the stream that feeds the famous Nevada Falls was losing water in unnecessary side cataracts, and sent a man up to "fix the falls." His spiritual descendants, who like to see everything tidied up and "under control," are still too numerous. One shudders at what some would do if given a free hand in any supposedly natural area.

Apart from the dilemma of maintaining the primitive in a world otherwise controlled by man, in every park and wilderness there is the problem of how to handle the people. Even if one could screen out the hoodlum and vandal, there would still be the necessity of coping with ever-growing numbers of visitors. Campgrounds, roads, and trails are bare necessities, but each detracts from the natural scene. Some visitors demand further amenities, dance halls and entertainments, so that they will not be bored by too much nature.

Part of the confusion lies in failing to separate public recreational areas from wilderness and natural preserves. A new art of recreation management on wild land is still in its early years. In areas where the public is encouraged to congregate, one must learn to handle the vegetation in such a way that maximum recreational value can be obtained

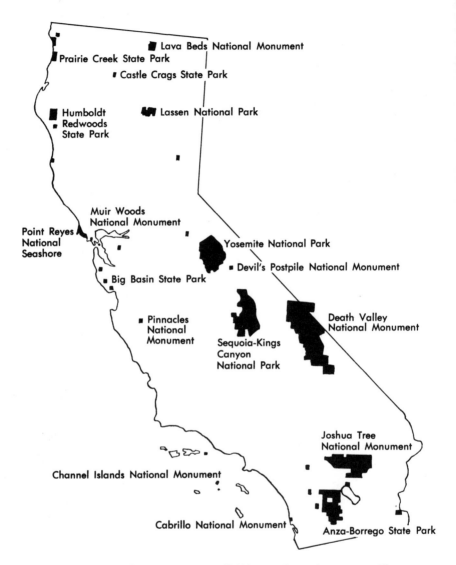

FIG. 13. Large areas of California have been set aside to preserve natural scenery, vegetation, animal life, and to provide recreation space. But with the drastic changes being felt in all other areas, many people feel that we have not yet reserved enough. The national parks and monuments and the larger state parks are shown here.

from each acre. In many of California's state parks, begun
with the idea of preserving the natural scene free from
disturbance, it has been found that recreational values were
lost through too much preservation. Now their rangers are
chopping and clearing to maintain 'open meadows where
people can walk, admire the vistas, or play, in place of the
dense woods that would crowd in were all interference
excluded. But these are only beginnings. It is necessary to
provide for bird watchers, wild-flower lovers, hikers, pic-
nickers, campers, fishermen, and all others with a legitimate
outdoor form of recreation to pursue. But the kind of management required in these areas of heavy public use must
be rigidly excluded from natural preserves and wilderness
regions where the objectives are different. Such areas can
be open only to those few who are willing to face the hard-
ships of wilderness travel. They cannot be permitted to
become mass recreation grounds. In these areas, however,
it will also be necessary to experiment to learn how best to
use or to exclude fire, how best to prevent insect and storm
damage, how best to control game populations, and all of
the other problems of wilderness maintenance in a world
that is no longer wild.

There have been times when many people have felt that
enough had been done toward preservation of the natural
beauty, vegetation, and animal life of California. Each
new area set aside was one new area removed from county
tax rolls, and each time the landowners of the county were
forced to assume a larger share of the burden of local or
state administration. But, faced with the appearance of
those portions of the state that have not been protected, it
is not easy to be complacent. It is true that nearly 7,000,000
acres of California land have been set aside and formally
preserved as park, reserve, or wilderness. Almost one acre

in every fourteen is dedicated by state or federal authority to recreational use or preservation. But, looked at another way, there is only one acre preserved for every 2.5 people in California. Perhaps a decade hence there will be 5 people to each acre of park or wilderness. How many people will there be for each wild acre in 2000 A.D., or 2500 A.D.? The decisions that are not made today perhaps cannot be made tomorrow. Areas that are not set aside now will be almost impossible to reserve in the future. Already it is difficult enough. Let even a whisper get around that an area is under consideration for purchase as a state or national park, and land speculators move in like vultures on a carcass. Land values miraculously climb until even the most conservation-minded legislature will balk at the sheer cost of the project.

It is worthwhile to look once more at the Prairie Creek Redwoods State Park, for there one can see the future. A wall divides the park from private land, a solid wall of ancient redwoods. Outside, all is devastation, stumps and debris, tractor trails, and gouged-out slopes. But this is only a normal scene, a reasonably well-managed logging operation. The visitor is told to console himself with the thought that this is a tree farm; it has been reseeded, and the redwoods will grow back. But if he thinks, he will realize that what will come back will be something new: the closely managed forest. There will be redwoods, true enough, but never again the ancient giants.

Extend the Prairie Creek scene over the entire state. Let every park or reserve be surrounded by intensively managed, logged-over, or otherwise exploited land. Away from the forest region, picture each of the existing parks surrounded by suburban housing, industrial plants, or commercial farming land. Realize, then, that for all future time the situation will not and can not be improved; things can only get worse. Does 7,000,000 acres then seem sufficient? What we do today must last forever. Perhaps there are a few more mountain lakes or chunks of chaparral that need saving. Perhaps we should not build another freeway down the shores of Lake Tahoe. Maybe there is some sagebrush or cactus desert, oak woodland or valley marsh, bold headland or quiet canyon that would be nice to have intact when tomorrow dawns. If they are not set apart from development, protected against the many abuses that a concrete-minded, bulldozer-oriented civilization can inflict on the land, they will not be here tomorrow. Perhaps it would not hurt now to do a little more. We could balance the cost by sending one less rocket into outer space. Earth, after all, is where we must live.

SEVEN

ORANGE BLOSSOMS AND
WAVING GRAIN

Today, "progress" too often outruns planning,
and the bulldozer's work is done before the
preservationist and the planner arrive on the
scene.   —STEWART L. UDALL *

M OST papers on world food problems include much
quoting of statistics of calories and protein needs or on com-
parative yields of grain. If I read too many of these, I find
myself thinking that food is some sort of uniform substance
like water that can be measured by the bowlful and distributed to the needy. Perhaps the day will come when
food will be much like that. It would be in the interests of
those who would simplify life to its bare essentials if this
were true, and those who expect science to solve the population problem with algal soup can look forward to this
day. Most of us are thankful that food is not so readily
reduced to such an easily measured substance. To even the
poorest American food is no simple thing. To most it is a
tasteful variety of items to be savored and enjoyed, a matter
of mealtime delight.

* *The Quiet Crisis.* New York, Holt, Rinehart and Winston, 1963.

In California, food is beefsteaks grown on the foothill ranges, marbled with fat in the feed lots. It is leg of lamb from valley pastures or pork chops from farm pens and woodlots. Food is lettuce from the Salinas and Imperial tomatoes mixed perhaps with avocados from the southern coastal plain. It is French bread baked in San Francisco from San Joaquin wheat flour. Food means apricots and cherries from the Santa Clara, oranges from Riverside, apples from Sonoma. There is nothing simple about it. Each item is important. Each has its special requirements for growth, and a particular complex of soils, climate, and topography that permits its production. I don't want to lose even one kind of fruit from the California list, or miss a single green onion or bell pepper from my salad. Perhaps from a global viewpoint I represent a spoiled, pampered minority, but I don't want to accept less. Thus it does me no good to hear that farm production in the United States is at its highest point—not unless I also know that things went well with the strawberries and peaches, and that plenty of peas and string beans have been produced. In the face of statistics on wheat and potatoes, therefore, I find myself concerned with the agricultural crisis in California, one that threatens the quality and variety in our diets in the years to come.

California is the leading farm state in the nation, with the highest annual yield of agricultural products. California is also one of the most highly urbanized states in the country, with over 80 percent of its people living in large metropolitan areas, and only a small fraction of its population actively engaged in farming. Two-thirds of the people live in the great urban complexes of Los Angeles and San Francisco, and most of these are remote indeed from the problems of farming production. This is, in part, the cause

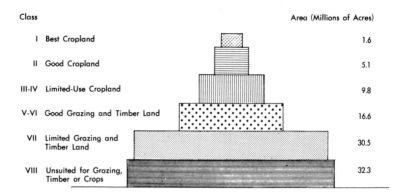

Class		Area (Millions of Acres)
I	Best Cropland	1.6
II	Good Cropland	5.1
III-IV	Limited-Use Cropland	9.8
V-VI	Good Grazing and Timber Land	16.6
VII	Limited Grazing and Timber Land	30.5
VIII	Unsuited for Grazing, Timber or Crops	32.3

FIG. 14. Good farming lands are scarce in California. The best croplands are being destroyed by uncontrolled urban-industrial growth. *Source: U.S. Soil Conservation Service system of land classification from Wohletz and Dolder,* Know California's Land, *1952*

of the trouble. It is far too easy for these people to think that food comes from the grocery store where it has been deposited by trucks that have hauled it from a food factory where it was produced by scientific magic. It is easy for city people, disregarding the variety in their diets, to think that science can solve food problems simply by devoting more factory space or more research to the job. It is easy to forget that food variety means farm variety, that farms take space and that crops are sensitive in their requirements. If it were not easy, surely we would not have the irrational spread of cities into farmlands, and the consequent disappearance under concrete and housing of some of our scarcest kinds of fruit- and vegetable-producing lands. Cities, after all, can be built on infertile or stony ground. They can expand upward instead of outward. Farmlands are more firmly fixed. They must be located on the fertile soils. They cannot move elsewhere without sacrifice of quality and increase in cost. Admittedly we could grow food in water, by hydroponics, or on sterile rock, by grinding it up and adding the

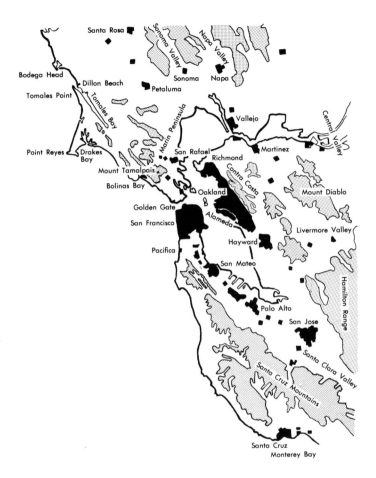

FIG. 15. Where things are in the San Francisco Bay Region. Highways, scattered housing, and commercial development occupy much of the space in between the communities shown. This picture represents the situation in 1950. In 1965 suburban growth connects Oakland with Hayward and extends on southward, with some gaps, as far as San Jose. Almost continuous urban, highway, and industrial growth extends along the west side of the bay from San Francisco southward beyond San Jose. The urban sprawl now covers much of the coastal land in the Pacifica region.

proper fertilizers, if cost were no object. But it makes far more sense to grow it on the best-quality soils, and the food produced is more likely to be fit to eat. The high cost of food today is in part a result of our forcing its production outward to the more marginals lands.

California is so well known for its specialized farm products that it hardly needs further publicity. It was started on the pathway to agricultural variety by the padres who used the gardens and fields of the missions to produce those fruits and vegetables brought with them originally from Spain and enriched by additions from the Aztec lands of Mexico. The first arrivals from the United States were amazed by the produce of the California mission lands. Some of them saw oranges and lemons growing for the first time, and most of them had never before encountered such items as olives, pomegranates, figs, or dates. The mission lands were the proving grounds for many of the crops that are now grown in the state, and give to it the greatest agricultural diversity in the nation.

The variety of climates and soils in California promotes the diversity of agriculture. The climates range from the dry subtropical of the south to the cool moist temperate ones of the north. The soils confound most broad-scale soil mappers, who usually lump them as "diversified soils of mountains and valleys." However, they include representatives of most of the major soil groups of the United States—the chernozems of the wheat belt, the prairie soils of the Middle West, and podzolic soils like those of the eastern forest region—along with many that are unique to California's Mediterranean-type climate. These are mixed into a complex mosaic, so that except in the larger valleys it is seldom possible to find large areas that are suited to one kind of crop.

Because of the peculiar land problems of California, farming on an intensive scale was slow in starting. The old Spanish land grants, the first private land in the state, were long devoted to livestock production. When the public domain was first made available to private claim, its disposition was touched by so much fraud and chicanery that it failed to encourage the small, farm homestead that was later to typify the farm belt of the Middle West. Instead, great privately owned agricultural empires came into being, typified by the holdings of Miller and Lux, or such major land monopolies as Southern Pacific or the Kern County Land Company. The corporation farm, owned by absentee landlords, was an early part of the California scheme. This in turn encouraged a kind of agricultural enterprise that received worldwide publicity only when the Russians, much later, tried it on the collective farms. Frank Norris, in his novel about the Southern Pacific land monopoly, *The Octopus*, describes a scene in the 1870's when thirty-five gang plows were driven like "a great column of field artillery" across the San Joaquin Valley, plowing one hundred and seventy-five furrows at the same moment. It cannot be said that such activity was farming in the sense of land husbandry. Rather, the soils of the San Joaquin Valley were mined for wheat, year after year without rest, until large areas were damaged, and winds gave rise to howling dust storms, later to be duplicated in the dust-bowl region of the Great Plains.

Much of the Central Valley fitted roughly into the category of "Swamp and Overflow" land. This was turned over to state ownership by the generous act of the federal Congress. State government, being at the time undistinguished for its integrity, allowed the lands to pass quickly into the hands of a few land monopolists who saw to it that the appropriate state officials were justly rewarded. It is said that Henry Miller of Miller and Lux had a team of horses pull a boat over areas of dry valley land, thus establishing, through witnesses, that he had traveled by boat over an area of "overflow" land. However, much of the valley was genuinely in the category of flooded land, and covered by great tule marshes. Its potentially productive land could not be claimed until drainage ditches and dikes were built. Such drainage, while creating some good farmland, had its effect upon water tables elsewhere in the valley, and contributed to the water crisis that was later to arise.

The great boom in wheat that began in the valleys during the 1870's continued for some decades. Other agricultural sprees were to get under way soon afterward. These in time led to the present diversified farming pattern, but at the start gave rise to some absurd developments. Thus, during the 1880's the idea that California would supplant Japan as the silk center of the world led to a great importation of silkworms and mulberry trees. Although the mulberries remain, the silk boom came to nothing. Next was a great promotion of cotton, and some brief success in the southern San Joaquin Valley, followed by failure through inability to acquire the needed agricultural labor. Cotton was to return after many decades, and California was ultimately to outproduce the South on the basis of cotton yield per acre, but the original investors in cotton land were badly hurt. At the same time that large scale wheat farming was getting under way, two Brazilian orange trees were planted at Riverside, California, by a Mrs. L. C. Tibbetts. Mrs. Tibbetts's oranges, which were seedless, were to displace the original Valencia orange of mission days and give California first place in navel-orange production. In the first decades of the orange bonanza, every Californian expected to have an orange tree or grove. Citrus trees were planted in the most unlikely localities, in places where commercial production, or even the ripening of fruit, could not hope to succeed. By the 1890's, however, oranges were dominating the economy of Southern California, and the former cow counties of the southland were well on their way to becoming agricultural and urban centers.

Many of California's specialized crops were grown by colonies of immigrants who brought with them from Europe or Asia the special techniques learned over the centuries in their homelands. Thus vineyards and wine making were to take over the foothills and coastal valleys of Central California, and rice fields were to dominate the economy of the lower Sacramento Valley. During the early days of agricultural establishment everyone had to learn "the hard way." The agricultural monopoly of a few people on the better farmlands forced many small farmers into marginal areas. There is hardly a mountain valley that has not been plowed at one time or another, before the inevitable failure drove the farmer away. Sometimes failure was slow in coming. Farms were established where crops could be grown during wet years but where they must fail during dry. Attempts to ride out the dry cycles, to wring a living from unsuitable soils, were to break the hearts of many farm families and do great damage to the land. Deserted homesteads and old farm buildings remain as decaying monuments to these endeavors in the back hills of the state.

At present agricultural production has largely retreated to the lands best suited for it. Cropland, in use for farm crops, temporary pastures, or temporary fallow, amounts to some 10,000,000 acres, or 10 percent of the total land area. Of this, approximately 55 percent is rated by the Soil

Conservation Service to be in Class I or Class II land. These are the best-quality farming lands, those that can be used without any unusual precautions to protect the soil, for year after year into perpetuity. Unfortunately, it is this best farming land that is now most endangered. It is estimated by Dana and Krueger that 90 percent of the population of California now lives on land that is actual or potential farming land. This is land that falls into the first four classes of the Soil Conservation system of classification, including in Class IV land suited to farming only with severe restrictions to protect the soil. It is also on this potential agricultural land that the greatest number of people will come to live in the future, unless they are prevented from doing so by some sort of community action. Up to the early years of World War II, nearly 2,000,000 acres of agricultural land in California had been converted to urban, industrial, or other nonagricultural usage. During the period 1952–1955, according to Soil Conservation Service figures, some 60,000 acres a year of farming land were being converted to nonagricultural use. A high percentage of this was being covered by suburbs, highways, airfields, and industries. Orchard, vineyard, and other specialized types of farm production were being particularly hard hit by this process.

In my childhood I used to be driven on Sunday trips to see the orchards in the Santa Clara Valley, at that time one of the principal centers of California fruit production. In the springtime we would drive through what seemed to be endless vistas of fruit trees in bloom. Here was the center for prune and cherry production. Here also grew plums, pears, peaches, apricots, and other fruit- and nut-bearing trees. Santa Clara fruit and other farm produce was exported over the nation and the world. Today the cities of

Santa Clara are importing far more than they export in the way of food. Only a deliberate effort on the part of Santa Clara County has saved any appreciable area for agriculture by zoning against urban-industrial development. But zoning laws are too easily repealed or set aside for one to feel any security in their mere existence. Unless backed by a public awareness of the problem, and an alertness to the activities of those who wish to convert orchards into building sites, zoning can represent only a temporary gesture. Between 1945 and the present the population of Santa Clara County increased more than threefold. During the same period the agricultural land decreased by more than one-third, and most of this decrease came in the better lands. Although some 50,000 acres of first-rate farmland are in a so-called "agricultural reserve," and zoned against urban development, they can be removed from it whenever a real-estate developer offers sufficient incentive and the public fails to oppose his action. Most of the areas I used to drive through now support houses instead of fruit trees. Unless the process can be halted, once for all, the farms will be pushed into the foothills through the spread of urbanization.

Up to 1955 we were losing farmland at a rate of 60,000 acres per year. Since 1955 the rate has speeded up. Despite all the protests and complaints from those who were aware of the problem, we are now losing it at a rate approaching 90,000 acres per year. We are expending incredible sums of money to bring new farming land into existence through vast irrigation developments, while at the same time we are concreting over better lands capable of more diversified food production.

There are those who still point to California's lead in agriculture, and mention the problem of farm surpluses.

Since to cope with the surplus we are retiring land from crop production, why should we worry about the conversion of some of it to urban use? The answer is partly in the question "What kind of land?" We don't need more potatoes or wheat, as yet. We do need land capable of diversified fruit and vegetable production. Furthermore, there is no guarantee that we can continue to expand per-acre production of crops, and thus compensate for the loss in agricultural acres. Technology has brought great gains in farm production, but its possibilities are not unlimited. A spokesman for the California Department of Agriculture, Dr. Elmer W. Braun, has pointed out that we cannot continue to expect science to compensate for our errors in land use. Improved technology cannot continue to bring increased gains in farm yield. If populations continue to grow, and farming land declines, the United States may well join the ranks of major importers of foods that it now produces and exports. This assumes that, through some miracle, other nations will still have food to export.

Houses can be built on barren rocky hillsides. Highways can be constructed on less valuable land. The short-term costs will admittedly be higher, but in any long-term view the benefits to be gained from keeping our best lands in farm production will more than balance any additional costs.

More than 3,000,000, and perhaps closer to 3,500,000, acres of actual or potential farming land in California have been converted to nonagricultural usage. By contrast, the Central Valley project for California, as originally designed, would have brought somewhat less than 1,500,000 acres under irrigation. The estimated ultimate cost for this original project (it has since been expanded) would have been somewhat more than $730,000,000. Perhaps it makes

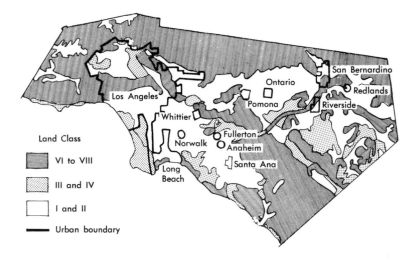

Land Class

VI to VIII

III and IV

I and II

Urban boundary

FIG. 16. Land classification and urban development in the Los Angeles area. Cities, towns, and highways have covered over much of the land best suited for growing crops. However, expansion of urban-industrial development into the nonagricultural land is beset with difficulties. Not only is it difficult to build and provide services for housing in the chaparral-covered hills, but the threat of fire sweeping through the brushfields is ever present. Fires, soil slippage, and mud flows have done great damage already to hillside homes. The actual extent of land covered by housing, highways, and other developments is far greater than can be shown on this map.

sense to pave over farmlands that are in production, and then spend millions to make arid lands suitable for farming. In somebody's reckoning it must pay off to build houses on orange groves in Los Angeles County, and then pump water down from Northern California to make oranges grow in Kern County.

Unfortunately, farming requires not just good soil but plenty of water. The amount of water needed in irrigation farming in arid lands is fantastic. It has been estimated that

5.7 acre-feet of water (more than 1,850,000 gallons) are required from a water source to make one acre of desert land produce crops. Not all of this is used directly by the growing crops. Some represents loss in distribution; some is the surplus needed to keep excess salts from accumulating in the soil of the irrigated land. Under California conditions an elaborate dam-and-canal system must be constructed to bring this water to develop new lands. An elaborate drainage system must be constructed to carry the excess, salt-laden water from the irrigated lands. Under present-day water-development schemes the costs of bringing the water over great distances and of developing the necessary installations is too great to be paid by the farmers who receive the benefits. Essentially they are subsidized by the developing agency. Furthermore the use of water is consumptive; the water cannot be reused. Industrial waste water can be reclaimed; water used for sewage disposal can be purified and reused. Irrigation water, however, except for the drainage excess, is fully utilized through evaporation and crop production, and is no longer available. It is sensible, in a water-deficient region, to keep those farm acres that are already in production intact, rather than make the sacrifices necessary to irrigate new lands. But in this respect California is not sensible. Whether it will become so before too late is doubtful.

California agriculture is big business. An investment of $100,000 in machinery alone is not uncommon on a single farm. The average farm size is close to 400 acres. Some of the large ones include many thousands of acres, but more than two-thirds are smaller, less than 100 acres. Relatively few are family farms, on which the family and one or a few permanent "hired hands" do all the labor. Most depend on the seasonal employment of farm labor. Migratory farm workers, who move from one agricultural district to another, aiding in the harvest of one kind of crop or another, have been almost a permanent feature of the California scene. At one time they were predominantly the "Okies," made famous in Steinbeck's *The Grapes of Wrath*. The native-born farm workers, however, have always been insufficient, and large numbers of Mexican nationals, *braceros*, have been brought to California to assist in farm work. Always the living conditions of these migratory workers has bordered on wretchedness. Strikes and violence have at times drawn attention to their plight. John Steinbeck dramatized these in his book *In Dubious Battle*. The situation has improved, somewhat, since then, but not much. However, the margin of profit on the smaller farm is not sufficient even today to enable the owner to invest too highly in farm labor. As an answer he has turned to mechanization, and the high investment in farm machinery is a result. The farmer lives in dread of unfavorable weather that can wipe out all his profits in a single year; he fights a constant battle against the pests encouraged where broad acreages are devoted to production of a single crop. Yet, despite the difficulties he has been successful; yields per acre have climbed, and America has not only been able to meet its own food needs but has also supplied the requirements of many less fortunate countries. The future of California depends on maintaining a healthy agriculture. The future of America depends to a significant extent upon the maintenance of productive farming in California, the leading farm state.

EIGHT

THE STRUGGLE
FOR WATER

To what purpose is industrialization if we end
up by replacing rigid confinement of man's
actions by nature with rigid confinement of
man's actions by man?   —HARRISON BROWN *

Aт one o'clock on the morning of May 21, 1924, the
inhabitants of Lone Pine in Inyo County were shocked
from their sleep by the blast of dynamite exploding nearby.
Just outside town concrete blocks were hurled into the air
as a major spillway of the Los Angeles aqueduct was
shattered. That rarest of California commodities, water,
was poured out on the desert sands. An aerial observer
might have noticed cars containing forty or more erstwhile
respectable citizens of Inyo County scattering from the
scene of the explosion. The first blast of the Owens Valley
war had occurred. During the following three years the
valley was to see continuing strife. Heavily armed guards
from the city of Los Angeles were to patrol its precious
aqueduct. Machine guns were to be mounted at strategic
posts along the waterway. Legal battles were to rage in

* The Challenge of Man's Future. New York, Viking Press, 1954.

the courts. Again and again the sound of high explosives would be heard as pipes, siphons, and spillways were blasted. Considering the quantities of firearms and explosives that were to be involved, it is surprising that no actual bloodshed took place. It was often threatened. The damage to property ran high.

The Owens Valley battle was the closest thing to a shooting war to develop during the long struggle for water in which California has been engaged. It was perhaps the most unsavory episode in a conflict that has brought out some doubtful aspects of human behavior. The basic issue in this conflict is one that has yet to be fully resolved: To what extent should one region be allowed to grow and accrue wealth at the expense of other regions? The growth of Southern California, more than any other region, has been subsidized with water drawn from, and at the expense of, much of the western United States.

It is difficult to find any really good reason why the city of Los Angeles should have come into existence. However, the padres found a suitable location there for a mission, and with the mission a pueblo grew. There was good soil for growing the fruits and grain needed to support the small populace, and all around was abundant rangeland, suited to the grazing of Spanish cattle. So the pueblo continued to exist after the mission had declined, a cow town in the middle of cow country. During the stormy days when California broke with Mexico, when the gold miners came, and when San Francisco boomed into a major city, Los Angeles remained a cow town. Its people and those of its hinterland were often out of step with the rest of the state. During the struggle for independence and then for admission to the Union, their sympathies were mostly with Mexico. During the Civil War, when California went with

Smith

Klamath Lake

Goose Lake

Klamath

Tule Lake

McCloud

Pit

Trinity

Mad

Eel

Eagle Lake

Honey Lake

Winnemucca Lake

Stony Creek

Sacramento

Feather

Pyramid Lake

Clear Lake

Yuba

Truckee

Lake Tahoe

Russian

Cache Creek

Napa

American

Walker Lake

Mokelumne

Stanislaus

Tuolumne

Mono Lake

Merced

San Joaquin

San Joaquin

Kings

Owens

Kaweah

Tule

Owens Lake

Salinas

Tulare Lake

Cuyama

Buena Vista Lake

Santa Ynez

Santa Clara

Salton Sink

Colorado

Alamo

the North, they were generally for the Confederacy. But the great drought of the 1860's put them out of the cattle business. The orange bonanza that had its start in the 1870's headed them toward a lead in agriculture. The completion of Southern Pacific's, and later Santa Fe's, rail connections with the East and South in the late 1870's and 1880's tied Los Angeles to the rest of the nation. Finally, the combination of climate and agricultural potential, when nationally publicized, started a flood of immigrants heading toward Los Angeles. This flood has never ceased for long, although there have been temporary interruptions to its flow. Consequently, Los Angeles became a city, then a metropolis, then a vast conurbation, and with each stage of its growth it has had to meet and overcome its greatest disadvantage—a lack of water.

Southern California is noted for its warm sunshine. Warm sunshine, however, is associated here with the absence of rain clouds. The climate that brings people to settle is the same that denies them the water necessary for their support. The average rainfall at Los Angeles is 15 inches; but in some years less than 5 and in others more than 40 inches fall. It thus alternates between drought and flood. At San Diego the rainfall averages less than 10 inches, but goes as low as 3 and as high as 27 inches in some years. Except for its mountains, Southern California has an arid or desert climate. But the mountains are high and steep—Mount San Jacinto towers up to nearly 11,000 feet

FIG. 17. Once the waters of California flowed without hindrance to the sea. But man could not adjust his ways to their seasonal pattern of flood and low water, nor could he be content to settle in places where water was abundant. The picture before dams and drainage is shown here.

above Palm Springs. The mountains gather rain but do not yield a steady stream flow to the lands below. Instead, because of their steep slopes, they give rise to sudden floods followed by long summers when the streams run dry. When fires sweep their brush-covered slopes, the soil from entire mountainsides may slip down into the valleys below. The coastal plain, however, is composed of deposits of gravels, sands, and other strata capable of holding and carrying water. With infiltration from the mountains exceeding the rate of underground flow to the sea, a surplus of water was available when the country was first settled. Shallow wells brought forth water under artesian pressure; more than enough to supply the small population of the early days.

Since the rain comes in winter when crops do not grow, the first settlers found a need for irrigation to produce orchard, vineyard, and vegetable crops. The Spanish padres constructed the first of the irrigation works, tapping the streams of the Sierra Madre. During the 1880's a number of irrigation-based colonies sprang up at San Bernardino, San Gabriel, Pasadena, Anaheim, and Riverside. The community of Redlands made a major step toward full development of local water sources by damming the Big Bear Valley in the San Bernardino Mountains in 1884. Big Bear Lake was to become a major recreational area as well as a source of irrigation water. A further effort in the 1890's led to the development of the attractive Lake Arrowhead in another high valley. Soon all the local communities were drawing on, and making full use of, the mountain water supplies.

By the 1890's Los Angeles was becoming a city and had already exploited its local watersheds and underground supplies thoroughly. In 1894 less than 8 inches of rain fell. For the next three years rainfall was below average, and in 1898 reached a low of less than 5 inches. For the succeeding six years, until 1905, it remained below average; but during all this time the city was growing rapidly. In 1903 a severe water famine hit. Consumption of water exceeded the recharging of the city's reservoirs, and only by drastic restriction on use was an actual catastrophe averted. During 1904 another severe crisis followed, and it became apparent that to maintain itself alone, even without further growth, Los Angeles would have to find a new source of water. At this time the man in charge of the city's water was William Mulholland, a person with unusual vision and initiative. The city engineer, a personal friend of Mulholland's, was Fred Eaton, who had long been familiar with the Owens Valley and had already investigated the possibility of bringing its water across the deserts to Los Angeles.

The Owens River drains most of the southern portion of the Sierra Nevada on the east side of the range. Towering above the valley are the highest peaks of the Sierra, peaks that gather moisture in even the driest years. The river flows through Inyo County's Owens Valley, and during historical times has emptied into Owens Lake, an alkaline desert lake from which the water evaporates once more into the desert air. Above the lake, however, the river flow permitted the existence of green and fertile lands. Originally these were developed as livestock ranges, but by the time that Los Angeles reached its first great water crisis, much of the flow of the Owens River was being used in the valley to support thriving farming communities based on irrigation. In 1902 the valley attracted the attention of the newly formed Reclamation Service, later to become the Bureau of Reclamation. Under the leadership of L. B. Lippincott, a friend of Fred Eaton, the Reclamation Service engaged in a survey of the irrigation potential of the valley, beginning in 1903. They found a suitable reservoir site at Long Valley, high on the Owens River, and apparently issued encouraging reports to the Inyo settlers about the future potential of their land. Into this hopeful atmosphere, however, the representatives of Los Angeles, Eaton and Mulholland, were to move in 1904.

The events of subsequent years are confused. The United States Reclamation Service, to the dismay and disbelief of the Inyo residents, suddenly issued a report stating that the proposed irrigation project for the Owens Valley should not be developed. Los Angeles agents, including Fred Eaton, quietly purchased land throughout the valley, with Eaton, acquiring the Long Valley reservoir site. Against the protest of the valley residents, President Theodore Roosevelt backed up the Reclamation Service, and further acted to extend the boundaries of the Inyo National Forest eastward. This protected from homestead entry land that might tie up further water within the valley, and provided space over which the aqueduct to Los Angeles might pass. In 1907 the city of Los Angeles voted a bond issue that made possible the construction of the Owens River aqueduct. Six years later, after an incredible feat of engineering, this aqueduct was built by Mulholland's men, across the Mojave Desert, and through desert mountain ranges, to pour water from the Owens River into Los Angeles reservoirs in the San Fernando Valley, more than two hundred miles away. To the disgust of the Inyo people, much of this water was not used initially to supply the needs of the city of Los Angeles, but went to irrigate the San Fernando Valley, where land that was once desert soared in value to $300 an acre or more, thus enriching those investors who had known in advance where the water would go.

Perhaps a crisis would not have developed had not a disagreement arisen between Eaton, who held the Long Valley reservoir site, and Mulholland, representing Los Angeles. Eaton asked a million dollars for his property; Los Angeles refused to pay. No dam was built; no reservoir was filled. Los Angeles and the Inyo people competed for the uncontrolled flow of the Owens River. Myriad minor irritations added to the difficulties, and so the Owens Valley war was started. The first round was in August, 1923, when armed citizens from the town of Big Pine prevented Los Angeles workmen from cutting off an Owens Valley irrigation ditch. From there the progress toward the first dynamiting was direct.

The Owens Valley struggle was not one of right against wrong, of white and black. There was justice on both sides, and chicanery on both sides. The valley people were motivated not just by a desire to maintain their homes, but by a desire to sell land at an inflated value. Personal profit motives spurred the activities of some city representatives. Eventually a fairly amicable agreement was reached, but not until after many had been badly hurt financially, and a lasting reservoir of ill will had been filled. Remi Nadeau, in *The Water Seekers*, marks one of the turning points in the struggle: the major disaster that struck Southern California in 1926. In that year one of the hastily constructed dams built to hold Owens Valley water gave way. A flood roared down the San Francisquito Canyon and into the Santa Clara River, crashing through several towns along the way. Before it reached the sea, 385 people had been killed and millions of dollars' worth of damage to property had been done. In the aftermath of this disaster, and a period of some soul-searching, Los Angeles passed a $12,000,000 bond issue to purchase Owens Valley land at peak prices. This quieted the conflict, and assured once for all that the water would come to Los Angeles. The Long Valley dam was built, and a reservoir to be known as Crowley Lake was filled. But by then Los Angeles had passed through several more water crises, and it was necessary to extend their acquisitions farther north, to tap the drainage of Mono Lake and bring these waters through tunnels into the Owens River system. Fortunately, this was accomplished with more foresight, better manners, and without conflict. By 1941, in time for the Second World War, the Owens-Mono system of water supply for Los Angeles was fully secured. By then, however, the entire supply was hopelessly inadequate for the city's needs.

To find a water source that would support the millions that were to come to Southern California, the residents of the southland, long before the Owens Valley issue was settled, turned their attention to the mighty Colorado, flowing through the desert on the eastern border of the state. Here was water drawn from the mountains of six western states, from as far north as Wyoming where the Green River flowed down from south of the Yellowstone; from the summits of the Colorado Rockies, which contributed the waters of the White, the Yampa, and the Gunnison; from New Mexico, which added the San Juan River to the flow. The Wasatch and Uinta mountains of Utah made their contribution; Nevada added its short desert streams; and Arizona poured the seasonal floods of the Gila into the muddy Colorado. Only California contributed no water to the stream, and California was the first to make major demands upon its waters. The first troubles developed with the Imperial Valley scheme.

The Imperial Valley, reaching north from the Mexican border, forms part of a great trough of land that sinks to more than 200 feet below sea level. North of it was the Salton Sink, a dry, salt-covered expanse. Farther north in the same trough was the Coachella Valley. The region was one of the most arid in California, and before the developers arrived, appeared on the maps simply as the Colorado Desert. Originally it had been a northward extension of the Gulf of California, but as the Colorado River built up its delta, this portion of the gulf was cut off from the rest. In time its waters evaporated, with those of the low-lying Salton Sink the last to dry out.

Imperial Valley attracted the attention of Charles Rockwood in 1896. Rockwood was an irrigation engineer; but, more than that, he was one of the imaginative, reckless entrepreneurs in which Southern California has specialized. Associated with him was George Chaffey, one of the best-known reclamationists of his day, whose name was associated with many successful irrigation projects. Both men realized that the Imperial Valley had fertile, alluvial soil. Both saw that only sixty miles away, flowing at a higher elevation, was all the water that would ever be needed to make it an irrigation farmer's heaven. Only a canal was needed to make the difference. This canal, Rockwood decided to build, and Chaffey, despite initial objections, was ultimately drawn into the plan. A promotion company, the California Development Company, was established. This company set about to raise the necessary capital. With lavish publicity it was possible to attract land-hungry farmers from all over the country who were willing to take up the barren desert acres, and contribute to the company, on the promise that water would be made available.

In 1900, Chaffey's men, with permission from no one, proceeded to tackle the Colorado just north of the Mexican border. Here they cut a canal from the river down into Mexico where they connected with the dry bed of the Alamo River that had once flowed into Salton Sink. Where this entered Imperial Valley the necessary diversion works and irrigation canals were built. Within only a few months the water from the Colorado had reached the Imperial Valley. The new Imperial farmers were busy sowing crops on irrigated lands soon afterward. By 1902 some 100,000 acres of land were under irrigation, and the early investors in land were in a position to either stay with farming or sell out for a profit. Meanwhile, however, the Reclamation Service in Washington had taken a cold view of the entire scheme. Calling into question the legality of claiming a large share of the Colorado flow, and the further legality of the land titles in the valley, the federal people threatened to close down the entire operation. Undismayed by this opposition, the California Development Company turned to the Mexican Government for assistance. Denied access to the Colorado in the United States, they obtained permission from Mexico to tap the river on the Mexican side of the border. For this permission they guaranteed that half of the water would be used to irrigate Mexican lands. Thus in 1904 the American canal was closed up and a new Mexican canal fed water into the Alamo River. At this stage, however, nature decided to intervene.

The Imperial Valley developers had not entirely understood the relationship of the Salton Sink to the Colorado delta. For many centuries the Colorado had shifted its flow from one delta channel to another. In time the silt deposited within a channel would raise its bottom to a high level, forcing the river to move over and cut a new channel. Although for a long time the river had flowed directly into the gulf, at various times in the past its flow had shifted over to the Alamo River or the New River and had, for a time, poured into the Salton Sink, converting it from a desert waste into a salty sea. The Mexican canal had been cut at just about the time when the Colorado would normally have been forced to make a channel shift. But the California Development Company spared it this trouble. When the floods rose in 1905, the Mexican canal was handy. Instead of receiving a portion of the Colorado River's water, it began to fill up with far more water than had been intended. As the flood waters came down from all the states of the Colorado Basin, the Imperial Valley farmers found that instead of an irrigation canal they were now the recipients of almost the full flow of the Colorado River. At the end of the flood season they found themselves the possessors of a new inland sea, the Salton Sea. In the process they had lost much agricultural land; they stood in danger of losing everything if the river continued to pour down upon them.

What followed was an epic man-against-the-river struggle that Remi Nadeau * has described in exciting detail. From 1905 to 1907 the fight went on. The finances of the California Development Company were exhausted in the first round against the river. Their efforts at diverting the flow were swept aside when the spring floods rose again. Next, the Southern Pacific Railway Company, under the leadership of Edward Harriman, threw its full resources into a struggle to save the valley. Guided by the skill of the company's construction engineers, and with an expendi-

* *The Water Seekers*. New York. Doubleday. 1950.

ture of over $2,000,000, the railway men, after many defeats, finally turned the Colorado back into its old channel. The personnel of this struggle seems strange to those who live in the middle of the twentieth century. The role of private enterprise in the battle is surprising today. Where were the army engineers? But in the first decade of this century the federal government could, and did, remain aloof from such an enterprise. It was not until 1910 that some federal money for flood control and levee work along the Colorado became available, and by then the Imperial Valley had already been saved.

In the agreement that the California Development Company made with Mexico—an incredible-enough circumstance when considered today—was the cause of future trouble. During drought years on the Colorado, it was impossible to supply water sufficient for both the Imperial Valley and Mexican lands. Once the old development company went out of existence, the Imperial farmers formed themselves into an Irrigation District, and as such sought permission to return once more to the United States side of the boundary to build an All-American canal on which Mexico could have no claim. In 1919 the Bureau of Reclamation gave its approval to this concept. By then, however, the whole issue of Colorado River water had entered into a new phase of controversy.

Before the question of an All-American canal could even be considered, it was necessary that some agreement be reached among the many states with a claim on the water of the Colorado. Southern California wanted water for irrigation and for its fast-developing metropolitan areas. In order to obtain this they favored the construction of a high dam to stabilize the river flow in its lower basin and prevent the cycle of abundance and scarcity that followed on high or low rainfall years. The proposed Boulder Dam, to be located in southern Nevada, would benefit California and Nevada, and a few small areas of Arizona. Most of Arizona and the rest of the Colorado states stood to gain nothing from its construction. Before they would vote for it, they insisted upon an allotment of the river water to provide for their future needs. Thus the representatives of Wyoming, Colorado, Utah, New Mexico, and Arizona were at times allied against the demands of California.

It was not until 1928, after many heated meetings of the water delegates of the various states, and many stormy sessions of Congress, that a bill was passed authorizing the construction of Boulder Dam. By then it had been generally agreed to divide the Colorado River flow halfway, allowing the upper Basin states half of the annual flow, and leaving the other half for California, Arizona, and Nevada. California's share was legally defined in the Boulder Dam law as 4,400,400 acre-feet,* and half of any surplus flow in the river. Unfortunately, the meaning of "surplus" was not clearly defined. Arizona insisted that in compensation for including the flow of its Gila River in the Colorado compact it was entitled to the extra million acre-feet represented by the flow of this river. California argued that no such understanding was included in the Act. No agreement between the states was ever reached. Many Arizonans believed that California was hogging and wasting water that could be used to cause an agricultural boom in Arizona. When the Los Angeles water district started work on an aqueduct across the Mojave to the Colorado, the concern in Arizona grew stronger. When work was started on

---

* An acre-foot equals 325,829 gallons of water, and represents one acre covered with one foot of water.

Parker Dam, needed to divert part of the Colorado flow into the Los Angeles aqueduct, the Arizona governor dramatized the opposition of his state by calling out the Arizona militia to prevent the dam from touching the soil of Arizona. Nevertheless, in 1935 Congress authorized the construction of this dam and the diversion of Colorado river water to Los Angeles. Since the future of both states was considered to be at stake, the legal struggle was to endure until 1963. In that year the Supreme Court finally ruled in favor of Arizona. California was authorized 4,400,000 acre-feet; Arizona, 2,800,000, and Nevada 300,000 of the "normal" 7,500,000 acre-feet of flow. Surplus was to include only the amount above 7,500,000, and not to include the million acre feet represented by the Gila River flow.

In 1935 the Colorado River was harnessed for the first time with the completion of Boulder Dam, and its dedication by Franklin Delano Roosevelt. Behind it was to build Lake Mead, a storage reservoir for 30,000,000 acre-feet, at that time the largest man-made lake in the world. Boulder Dam was a new element on the American scene, a giant multiple-purpose dam, to be used for the generation of electric power, for irrigation, domestic and industrial water supply, river channel stabilization, and recreation. It was the first of its kind to be completed by the United States Bureau of Reclamation, and set the pattern for all the multiple-purpose dams that were soon to follow on the major rivers of the West.

In 1941 Parker Dam was completed, and the aqueduct had been built across the forbidding terrain of the Mojave. At almost the same time as the Inyo-Mono water system was completed, the first Colorado River water flowed into Lake Matthews. Southern California had sufficient water

Yosemite, the secret valley, the hiding place of Indians. *National Park Service*

John Muir, who began the fight to save the pieces of wild California and who founded the Sierra Club that continues this fight today. *Culver Pictures, Inc.*

Fern Canyon in Prairie Creek State Park. A freeway over it, or beside it, has been proposed.

A wall of redwoods divides the state park from the private land outside. Outside, all is devastation, yet it represents a reasonably well-managed redwood logging operation.

Civilization crowds the edges of the remaining wild places. Yosemite National Park. *National Park Service*

Deserts have their own stark beauty. This has been preserved in such areas as the Death Valley National Monument. *National Park Service*

The unique qualities of the neglected Channel Islands was recognized with the establishment of the Channel Islands National Monument. *National Park Service*

Following World War II, the suburban spread into the hills and valleys south of San Francisco began. *Wide World Photos*

Every year fires sweep the chaparral-covered hillsides of California. Here the expensive Bel-Air section of Los Angeles is shown after the 1961 brush fire that destroyed it. *Wide World Photos*

A massive rebuilding is taking place in the heart of San Francisco as part of the urban renewal program. One can only hope that this will bring new life into the central city without damage to its unique character. *Wide World Photos*

Downtown Los Angeles, the city that surrendered to the freeway system. *Wide World Photos*

The urban fringe creeps outward into farm land and orchard.
Used-car lots, junk yards, billboards, and shacktown blight the
approaches to the cities.

One freeway leads to another, as the first becomes jammed with
traffic, but we accept no limits to the number of motor vehicles.
Wide World Photos

The beach at Santa Catalina. Everywhere, crowding destroys the
values that the people who crowd in came to seek.

Lake Tahoe. We cannot afford to shatter the beauty of this scene with yet another freeway. *Photograph by Tom Myers; courtesy of California Division of Beaches and Parks*

People flock to scenes like this in Disneyland, an artificial world to take the place of what we are everywhere else destroying.

Wild country forms a bulwark for human freedom. These granite peaks and glacial lakes may prove to be our most valued asset in tomorrow's crowded world. *National Park Service*

to fight the Second World War, to attract the aircraft and shipbuilding industries and the workers needed to staff them. One might assume that with the watershed of half the Rocky Mountains and the southern Sierra at its disposal, along with its local mountains, Los Angeles and its companion cities would be content. But this was not to be true. Populations continued to boom, and World War II had hardly ended before new water crises arose in the southland. San Diego was saved from catastrophe only by the arrival of its share of Colorado River water. In 1947 and 1948 Santa Barbara went dry, and avoided catastrophe only by the most rigid rationing. Southern California had only one more direction to look for water, northward beyond the Tehachapis. There the new Central Valley Project was channeling the water from much of Northern California, and directing it southward.

When the Central Valley was first seen by the Spanish, it bore little resemblance to the valley of today. It was then described as a tule valley or valley of lakes, but there are few of the tall rushes and no lakes in the areas that the Spanish first observed. The valley receives the drainage of the west side of the Sierra in a series of major streams, starting with the Kern River in the south, draining down from the Mount Whitney country, and ending with the Pit River in the north, cutting across the Sierra divide from the Modoc country. North of the Pit the Sacramento River picks up the drainage from Mount Shasta and the Trinity Mountains to the west. Only a few small streams drain into the valley from the Coast Ranges, such as Cache Creek that comes down from Clear Lake. The southern end of the valley is essentially desert where it is not flooded by the rivers, since the annual rainfall is only five inches. Here the Kern once flowed into Buena Vista Lake, an interior basin that served to charge the underground water tables. Farther north the Tule, the Kings, and the Kaweah came down from the Sequoia country to fill Tulare Lake. Still farther north the San Joaquin drained a broad area of the high Sierra, reached the valley floor, and moved slowly northward to reach its delta in San Francisco Bay. Along its route it picked up the Merced from Yosemite, and the Tuolumne, Stanislaus, and Calaveras from the Gold Rush country. These were the rivers of the San Joaquin Valley, the drier half of the Central Valley, flooded in the northern portion during the season of spring runoff, and covered with extensive tule marshes at all times.

The northern Central Valley is the valley of the Sacramento. South from the Pit this river picked up the waters of the Feather, the Yuba, and the American rivers that drained from most of the northern Sierra. The Sacramento carried far more water than the San Joaquin because it drained from the high rainfall areas of the north. It too lost itself in a maze of tule swamps that extended northward from the broad delta where it flowed into the bay.

One of the first good descriptions of the San Joaquin Valley was provided by Lieutenant George Derby who explored it in 1849–1850. He described Tulare Lake as a body of water approximately twenty miles long, connecting to the south with an extensive swamp approximately fifteen miles long by ten in width. The entire lake was surrounded by a wide band of tules, making it difficult for him to reach the open water. Away from the lake the surrounding countryside was described as barren, sandy desert to the east and south. Westward, where the rivers drained in, there was good grassland. South from Tulare Lake a slough sixty miles long connected it with overflow from Buena Vista Lake, which was also described as being sur-

rounded by sterile, unproductive country. Buena Vista
Lake was found to be ten miles long and approximately
five wide in May, 1850. North of Tulare Lake another
broad slough connected it with the San Joaquin River. In
May, 1850, the entire country between the lake and the
river was covered with a vast swamp. One hundred years
after George Derby visited this area one could find no
Tulare or Buena Vista Lake. The sloughs and marshes
had been drained. The west side of the valley was still
barren and desolate, but the east was the site of orchards
and fields supported by irrigation waters from the rivers
that once drained into the lakes and moved northward,
through sluggish sloughs and swamps, to the bay.

After the settlement of the Central Valley many of its
farms and towns came to depend upon its artesian waters.
Shallow wells originally tapped a vast underground supply. But with the drainage of the valley and the corralling
of its rivers, the rate at which this underground reservoir
was refilled was slowed down. The steady demands of irrigation lowered the water table, in places for many hundreds of feet, so that deep pumping became necessary, and
the skills developed in drilling for oil became employed in
searches for the ever-shrinking supply of underground
water. During the 1940's and 1950's it was thought that
the valley farmers were mining underground water that
dated from the Pleistocene ice ages, instead of drawing
upon current production. Sinking of the land followed
water table lowering. This was to become a major problem
that threatened roads and railways, buildings, and the new
shiny canals of the Central Valley Project.

The water troubles of the San Joaquin Valley led inevitably toward schemes for water development that involved shifting water from the Sacramento Valley, where

floods had long been a serious problem, to the San Joaquin, where drought held sway. The idea of a Central Valley development dates back to 1874 when a survey and water plan was worked out by Colonel B. S. Alexander. But in those years, massive water developments were still unnecessary, and they were staunchly opposed by such land monopolists as the Southern Pacific Company, and by private power companies who had vested interests in existing water developments. In 1919 the subject was renewed when Colonel Robert Marshall of the Geological Survey came forth with a scheme for water development to supply the southern valley and ship water to Los Angeles. In its broad features, Marshall's plan resembled the Central Valley development that was to come.

In 1933 the California state legislature passed a Central Valley Project Act, based on a state water plan developed from Marshall's original ideas. This act authorized the issuance of $170,000,000 in bonds to finance the project, but was actually passed with an eye to federal financing. These were depression days, and federal funds were flowing through the country more freely than water in an attempt to put the nation back on its feet. The California water bonds were not sold. Instead, in 1935, the federal Bureau of Reclamation received funds from Congress to begin work on the project. The central feature of the plan was the shifting of water from the surplus areas of the northern valley southward to the dry areas of the San Joaquin. The key structures were to be Shasta Dam, to be built north of Redding on the Sacramento and stabilize the flow of this river, and Friant Dam, to be built on the San Joaquin for the purpose of cutting off its flow and diverting it southward instead of northward. In 1937 ground was broken for construction of Shasta Dam.

As developed by the Bureau of Reclamation, the Central Valley Project was opposed by the private power companies, noteworthily the Pacific Gas and Electric Company, and by the larger landholders of the Central Valley. It also brought out the long-standing, if unofficial, opposition between the Bureau of Reclamation, concerned with irrigation and power, and the United States Army Corps of Engineers, concerned with flood control and navigation. The latter group had the blessing of power companies and land monopolists, since it did not compete or interfere with their activities. The Bureau, however, proposed to sell public power directly to municipalities. Furthermore, the Bureau was governed by a 160-acre limitation on the distribution of its irrigation water. Essentially, therefore, water could not be made available to the larger landholdings. These, if they wished to use federally produced water, would have to dispose of their lands at prices determined before irrigation water became available. Consequently, there was an all-out attack on the Bureau of Reclamation during the early development of the Central Valley Project. In a particularly vitriolic form, this attack was presented in a book by Senator Sheridan Downey of California, published in 1947, with the title *They Would Rule the Valley*. The "they" in question were the bureaucrats of the Department of the Interior who were singled out individually, from Secretaries of the Interior, Ickes, and Krug, down through the lower echelons, and condemned as being inefficient, uninformed, or downright corrupt. The opposite point of view was presented in the following year in a book by Robert de Roos, entitled *The Thirsty Land*. In this, the Pacific Gas and Electric Company, Kern County Land Company, and other land and power interests were presented as being obstacles to the welfare of the nation. There would be little value in reviving these old issues in this book. Despite all the noise, the Central Valley Project was built.

By 1951 all the features in the initial Central Valley proposal had been put into operation. First the monumental Shasta Dam blocked off the flow of the Sacramento and formed a major geographical feature on the California landscape, Shasta Lake, backing up thirty-five miles along the river canyons behind the dam. From Shasta Dam water poured through power generators into the river below. There Keswick Dam was built to stabilize the flow of the river between periods of peak power release and times of low power needs. Below Keswick, the Sacramento, cooler and clearer than in its old, uncontrolled days, flowed south through the valley. Far to the south, Friant Dam put a finish to the San Joaquin as a valley river. From Friant its entire flow was diverted to the southern valley through two giant canals, the Madera Canal and the Friant-Kern Canal, to meet the irrigation needs of this arid area. To replace the waters of the San Joaquin in its valley channel, the Sacramento is transferred, in part, at its delta by means of the Delta Cross Channel that carries it fifty miles to Tracy. Here Central Valley power moves giant pumps that lift the Sacramento into the Delta-Mendota Canal. This carries it for 120 miles, and after irrigating lands along the way, it is dumped into Mendota Pool below Friant Dam on the old San Joaquin River. There Sacramento water flows down the San Joaquin riverbed in replacement for San Joaquin river water to meet the needs of the lower valley. The entire system sounds as though it was devised by the Red Queen in Alice in Wonderland, but actually represents an engineering masterpiece, and truly does make sense. Through this elaborate scheme the water-rich streams of Northern California supply the needs of the water-deficient southern region.

Before the initial Central Valley Project had been completed, it was, like all other water developments that have been constructed, obsolete. After World War II it was apparent to all that the enormity of the task of developing California water was so great that there was no room for feuding between state and federal interests. All available funds would be needed. In 1956 a new California Department of Water Resources was established to handle the state's responsibility for the job. This agency took over certain phases of the new water program; the Bureau of Reclamation assumed responsibility for other new construction, and the Army Engineers undertook their share of the work. In 1957 a new California Water Plan was submitted to the legislature by the Department of Water Resources. In its scope it made the original Central Valley Project seem like a minor operation.

Today dams stand on most of the major rivers draining into the Central Valley, and are proposed or are under construction on all the others. Two major operations under way include the Feather River Project, being carried forth by the state, and the San Luis project of the federal government. The state project will pen up the largest remaining free river in the Sierra, and transfer Feather River water southward. The San Luis project will make possible the transfer of water from the Feather and other northern rivers southward along the west side of the San Joaquin Valley, to irrigate lands along the way, and ultimately to be moved by a state canal across or around the Tehachapis to supply the needs of Southern California communities as far south as San Diego.

Further developments in the state plan for water include the shipment into the Central Valley and Southern California of much of the water from the major coastal rivers of Northern California. The Trinity, the Eel, the Mattole, and the Klamath, streams that rise in the high rainfall belt of the north coast and that once flowed directly to the ocean, will be dammed and pumped backward, using power generated by giant dams being built as part of the system. Trinity Dam already blocks the upper Trinity, and water from here is now diverted by way of Whiskeytown Reservoir over the mountains to the Sacramento system. In the final phase of the water plan every drop of water that falls on most of California will enter into the scheme in one way or another. The old wild river systems will cease to exist. But vast as the state water plan is, it dwindles into insignificance before the still vaster plan advanced by the United States Department of the Interior. Under the new Udall water plan for the southwestern United States, every watershed of consequence is considered, and California would be forced for the first time in history to give up some of its surplus water to meet the needs of other western states. This prospect does not please many Californians.

During all this expenditure of hundreds of millions of dollars, and this changing of the California landscape, there has been an occasional voice that asked the question: Why? But it has either not been heard or has been answered with the obvious reference to "needs" for power, irrigation, municipal and industrial water supply, flood control, and so on, to meet the requirements of a growing population. Since growth is by definition progress, and progress is by definition good, this is deemed to be answer enough for any but a fool.

It is indeed difficult to oppose or criticize the water-development schemes. At first glance it seems all to the good. If conservation means "wise use" of resources, is it not wise to transfer water from areas of excess and waste to areas of shortage and need? The bringing of irrigation water makes the desert bloom and causes land values to soar. Domestic water supplies are obviously essential. So long as populations continue to grow and water can be made available, it must be made available. Industry also requires water, and the development of industry not only provides support for the people, but makes possible the high material standard of living to which we have become accustomed. The big dams constructed to provide water also provide power, another essential for farms, cities, and industries. Dams also stabilize river flow, improve channels for navigation, and, except in unusual years, prevent disastrous floods. Furthermore, no one who has lived in the West can question the recreation value of the new reservoirs. A dam is hardly completed before people are flocking in with their fishing poles, power boats, water skis, and all the other paraphernalia used for water sports.

The agencies charged with water development, both federal and state, have done their job well both in planning and in construction. The engineering miracles they have been asked to perform, and have performed, have been world marvels. Assuming what they must assume, that populations will continue to grow and their needs must be met, they have come up with the necessary answers in water development. It is not their job to consider the whole philosophy behind the development of California's resources. Their job is to provide water.

Nevertheless, the California water plan has been and should be criticized and questioned. It has been pointed out by some that the damage done by proposed water

Trinity
Dam

Shasta Dam

Clear Lake

Berryessa
Dam

Oroville Dam

Folsom Dam

Delta
Project

Hetch
Hetchy

Delta-Mendota Canal

San Luis
Dam

Friant Dam

Los Angeles Aqueduct

Friant-Kern Canal

Pine Flat
Dam

West Side Canal

Lake Mead

Nacimiento Dam

Hoover Dam

Isabella
Dam

Davis Dam

Proposed Tunnel
and Canal to
Southern California

Parker
Dam

Cachuma
Dam

Colorado
Aqueduct

Lake Matthews

Coachella Canal

San Diego Aqueduct

Salton
Sea

All-American
Canal

Alamo Canal

developments sometimes far outweighs any conceivable gain. Objections to various dams, canals, or proposed uses of water have come from many sources. Among the first to wage an all-out war against a proposed dam and reservoir were some who liked nature the way it was, who did not want to see a wilderness destroyed. Thus, long ago, in 1901, there was the fight over Hetch Hetchy.

In 1901 the city of San Francisco was beginning to run out of water. In searching for a source of municipal water, its engineers came across what seemed to be a really excellent location for a dam in a place called Hetch Hetchy Valley on the Tuolumne River. The city filed for permission to build a dam and fill a reservoir on this site and evidently expected little difficulty in obtaining it. However, Hetch Hetchy was a little Yosemite Valley, and lay within the boundaries of the newly created Yosemite National Park. Furthermore, it was, along with the Grand Canyon of the Tuolumne above it, one of the favored haunts of John Muir, then the outstanding conservationist of the West and the first leader of California's battling Sierra Club. To John Muir a Hetch Hetchy reservoir would be an abomination—unthinkable. He immediately called the issue to the attention of the Secretary of the Interior, who in turn promptly denied San Francisco's request. But the city was not prepared to be denied. What followed was the first big fight between two schools of conservation thought that were and still are active in America.

FIG. 18. Today only a few small streams run unhindered to the sea. Some of the old lakes and rivers have disappeared. Dams, reservoirs, canals, and aqueducts dominate the California landscape. *Source: Bureau of Reclamation and California Dept. of Water Resources (including projects under construction)*

On one side of the Hetch Hetchy battle, allied with San Francisco, were the men who thought of conservation as the development and wise use of resources for the greatest material good of society. These are the men behind the drive for sustained-yield forestry, contour plowing on the farm, multiple-purpose dams for water development, conservative grazing of rangelands, and related programs. On the other side were the "preservationists," the backers of wilderness, national parks, and preserves, who think that beauty is worth saving for its own sake and for the aesthetic appreciation of generations of people to come. In the Hetch Hetchy issue, the first group was represented by some of the leading men in the history of conservation in America, Gifford Pinchot, America's leading forester, and Theodore Roosevelt, naturalist, outdoorsman, and at that time President of the United States. At Pinchot's recommendations, Roosevelt overrode the ruling of the Secretary of the Interior and authorized the construction of the Hetch Hetchy project. But the fight was not over. Congress provided the next battleground.

John Muir spoke and wrote eloquently about the beauties of the Yosemite of the Tuolumne—"no holier temple has ever been consecrated by the heart of man." But the people were not listening. In the halls of Congress the voice of practicality was heard. In 1913 Congress moved to authorize construction of the Hetch Hetchy project. John Muir, crushed by the defeat, was to die the following year. The Sierra Club, however, lived on to fight again. As the crush of population grows and the shortage of Yosemites becomes apparent, those who support the Sierra Club viewpoint grow in numbers. Nevertheless Hetch Hetchy was a disturbing defeat. A Yosemite National Park with a dam sets a precedent for dams in other parks. Considering all that has passed since John Muir's time, there seems no excuse for Hetch Hetchy. It was not the only possible site for the dam, only the cheapest and most practical of those examined. For a little extra cost, Yosemite Park and Muir's little valley could have been saved. But it is not the fault of the water developers. If they think that Grand Canyon, Yosemite Valley, or Heaven itself would make a good storage reservoir, they are paid to say so. The public has the responsibility for saying No.

Opposition to water developments has come, fairly consistently, from fisheries interests. Commercial fishing is a multimillion dollar industry based on sustained harvesting of a renewable resource. Sport fishing is a favored sport of a high percentage of Americans. Dams, reservoirs, and canals can and have changed the entire aquatic environment for freshwater and sea-run fish. Fish cannot bypass the larger dams. Fish ladders are impractical on the high dams. Where they can be used to get the mature fish upstream to spawn, they are of no use in getting the juvenile fish back downstream on their journey to the sea. Even smaller dams and irrigation canals create hazards. Migrating fish end up in some farm canal where they cannot survive. Furthermore, dams change such important factors in the environment as water temperature and available nutrients. A clear, cold trout stream can be changed into a warm-water lake. Since the economic value of fisheries is obvious, the objections of fisheries experts have had to be considered by the dam builders.

The construction of Shasta Dam seemed to threaten the highly valuable salmon run of the Sacramento River. There was no hope of bringing adult fish, migrating from the ocean, upstream to spawn above the high dam. Consequently the dam would deny the vast area of spawning ground on the upper Sacramento and its tributaries to the salmon, and it was expected that the salmon-fishing industry would suffer a severe decline. However, the Bureau of Reclamation, as part of its construction plan, included a major fish hatchery, built below the dam, to produce salmon to take the place of those lost through denial of access to the headwater streams. It was hoped that this would at least cut the loss to the fishery. When the dam was completed, however, and the hatchery in operation, it was found that salmon production in the Sacramento had actually increased. The steady flow of cool, silt-free water from the dam improved the quality of the lower Sacramento for salmon. Survival of wild fish produced on the lower tributaries, as well as of hatchery fish, was enhanced, and there was a net gain to the fishery. Something had been lost. A hatchery fish is not a wild fish, but in this instance such an aesthetic consideration could be ignored.

When dams go up on all the rivers, when all the water is channeled and controlled, one cannot expect that the Shasta Dam experience will be repeated. The total effect upon sea-run fisheries will be adverse. Hatcheries can compensate in part. Improvements on those streams, or portions of them, that are still accessible to fish can help some. But there is little hope that the production of salmon, striped bass, steelhead, and other sea-run species can be kept at the level of earlier years. Furthermore, the Department of Fish and Game and federal Fish and Wildlife Service need to be constantly alert to see that any provision is made for fisheries. Dam builders tend to forget about fish. Water is highly in demand, and there is always a battle to see that some minimum flow below the dam is provided in the water plan. To some, the losses in fisheries seem an argument against dams. To others, the enhanced production of fish in the big reservoirs behind the dam seems more than to compensate. Admittedly the reservoir fish are of different species, resident fish rather than migratory, sometimes warm-water fish rather than trout and salmon. But there is no doubt that they provide recreational fishing, often in higher quantity than was available before.

Water developments also affect the wildlife of the land. One of the more important waterfowl areas in California was the grasslands region located near Los Banos in the central San Joaquin Valley. When the Central Valley Project was first completed, no provision was made to supply water to this wildlife area. Demands for such water met opposition from those who had figured on every available acre-foot for some other use. Fortunately, in this instance the agencies involved were able to get together. Water was finally provided, and the waterfowl breeding and wintering area was restored. But each new development brings new problems. The state is now fighting to keep a water flow to its important Gray Lodge waterfowl refuge, one of the oldest and more interesting in the state. The Department of Fish and Game now has a topflight team of biologists working on the proposed water developments for the Delta region of the Sacramento to see that the necessary provisions are made to safeguard the wildlife in that region. Unfortunately, the ultimate effect of water developments on the wildlife of California is hard to predict, if not impossible. We are making major environmental changes. Everything that lives in California will feel the effects.

There are those who point out the undeniable truth that our entire scheme of dams and reservoirs is necessarily short-lived. Without attention to careful management of the lands above the dam, and sometimes even with it, the reservoirs must inevitably fill with silt, lose their storage capacity, and eventually become useless. The efforts of the city of Santa Barbara to secure a water supply give unusually striking support to this viewpoint. In 1920 Gibraltar Dam was built on the Santa Ynez River behind Santa Barbara. Within a short time it was evident that the reservoir behind the dam was filling with silt. Two more dams were built upstream to collect the silt and debris. Within two years after their completion, they had been completely filled with silt. Twenty-five years after its completion, the storage capacity of Gibraltar Dam had been reduced 50 percent, and it was inadequate to meet the water needs of Santa Barbara. After the severe water crisis of 1947 and 1948, Santa Barbara sought a new answer to its problems, and a newer and larger structure, Cachuma Dam, was built downstream from Gibraltar. However, fires still burn on the chaparral-covered watersheds, and after each fire soil moves downhill to be carried eventually into the quiet waters of the reservoir. If we continue careless practices of land use on our major watersheds, our entire reservoir system will someday be converted into a series of flat alluvial plains through which the old rivers will cut their channels as they flow to the sea.

Objections to the state water-development plan also come, realistically, from the areas from which the water is to be taken. The Owens Valley battle illustrates this point. Los Angeles is permitted to grow. The Inyo-Mono country is not. Once the decision was made to ship Inyo-Mono water to Los Angeles, once the dams were constructed and the aqueducts were built, the decision became virtually irrevocable. Perhaps for the Owens Valley this was all for the best. It has remained a pleasant place. Life in Los Angeles grows more intolerable. But one can question the wisdom of similar decisions applied to all the water-rich regions of Northern California. We insist that water must be shipped to the places where people and industry have located. We could equally well insist that people and industry should locate in the areas where water is available. It would have been easier to develop a major harbor in Humboldt Bay than to build an artificial harbor for Los Angeles. The rail lines and highways could have been routed to Eureka as well as to Southern California. Eureka and Northern California have water. Why encourage further industrial and population growth in Southern California through shipping that water over hundreds of miles? The only answer to this is political. Southern California has the votes.

If we look to the future, the wisdom of our water-planning schemes becomes even more doubtful. Inevitably an end must be reached, when there are no more rivers to dam and no more water surplus to be shifted. When this time comes, either growth must cease or we must find some new way of providing water that differs from the dam-and-canal system we now use. If this is true, then should not the growth cease, or the new way be found before we have ruined our scenic areas, crippled our wildlife and fishery resources, and permanently inhibited the development of broad areas in the state? Will Southern California truly be a better place to live when it has 20,000,000 people instead of 10,000,0000? Will we really be better off when we have paved over all of the orange groves of Los Angeles, and developed new ones in the desert? Not even the most ardent developer can truly answer Yes to either question. Why, then, do we proceed with the state water-development plan?

Let us look first at the question of new ways for finding

water. The most obvious place to look for it is in the original source, just offshore from Southern California's cities, the ocean. There is nothing new about the idea of desalting ocean water for use on land. The general techniques have been known for centuries. On a small scale, desalinization has been in use for decades. On a broad scale, as an economically feasible operation, there is much to be learned. Some research has been aimed at the problem since man first encountered water problems in seacoast communities. Large-scale research is a product of the past twenty years, and only in recent years has it produced significant results. Methods in use include distillation, freezing, electrolysis, and filtering of seawater. Already the city of San Diego has received desalted ocean water from a plant constructed under the auspices of the Office of Saline Water of the Department of the Interior. This plant, using a distillation process, produces 1,400,000 gallons of fresh water each day. While this is an impressive figure, it represents less than five acre-feet of water per day. The daily needs of San Diego, now met mostly from the Colorado River, are 57 times greater than this figure. Furthermore, the cost of production is now $1.25 per thousand gallons of desalted seawater, and can be cut, at best, to an estimated $0.60 per thousand. The cost of bringing water from the Feather River is said to be only $0.23 per thousand gallons.

However, the high costs of desalted water represent the shortcomings of present methods and the limited output of plants now in use. The Department of the Interior has plans for two plants in Southern California that would each produce 25,000,000 gallons of water per day. The use of nuclear power in future developments could cut the costs still lower. Since the oceans are the only source of a relatively unlimited water supply, further efforts in this direction are fully justified even though costs remain high and the benefits, for a time, limited.

In a study of the desalting problem published under the auspices of the Conservation Foundation, it was concluded that a seawater conversion plant processing 1,000 million gallons of water per day was both possible and practical.* Such a plant could supply the daily needs of a city as large as Los Angeles and would equal the daily output of the Colorado River aqueduct. Within a relatively short time, given adequate funds for research and pilot projects, such a plant could produce fresh water at a price within the reach of cities and industries, although at a higher price than could be afforded by irrigation farmers. A price of $0.30 per thousand gallons was considered feasible for seawater processing. For irrigation purposes this is too high. However, conversion of brackish waters from estuaries, or the purification of salt-laden drainage water flowing from irrigated lands, could be done at a cost far lower than the desalting of seawater.

Considering the prospects from seawater conversion, and the obvious disadvantages associated with full implementation of the system of dams and canals for movement of fresh water over California, would it not be wise to slow down on our dam building? It is estimated that if all the streams of Northern California are fully developed, the water needs of Southern California can be met for the next twenty-five years. After that, what? Seawater conversion is the only answer. Why not make it the answer now? The reasons are obvious. We do not really plan for population at all. People move without restraint and reproduce without concern. Populations grow and populations vote.

* Cecil B. Ellis, *Fresh Water from the Ocean* (New York, Ronald Press, 1954).

Growth may be recognized as unwise; but people come anyway, and, having arrived, demand water. Since more people mean more votes, they will have the water. It is not within the power of a democratic state government to set a ceiling on growth unless the people want it. The people, as yet, do not realize fully the implications of their demands for water.

John Muir, in his final words on Hetch Hetchy, said "They will see what I meant, in time. . . ." But the time is not yet here. The forces behind water development grow stronger with every victory, and they have won every battle. They are now an irresistible juggernaut moving across the American landscape, changing it and shaping it to a pattern that will prevail through all the future. They have only one argument: they will bring dollars into the hands of those that control land and industry. That is the only argument they need. Against the prospect of increased material wealth for the majority of the voting public, against the needs of an ever-expanding economy, all other arguments fail.

What can be done? Those who do not consider growth and progress as synonyms for good will waste their time in opposing the broad plan for California water development. They will be a fly attacking an elephant. Those who favor water development are used to brushing aside and crushing underfoot the interests of the preservationists. Flies do not kill elephants, but many flies can keep elephants out of some woods. It is up to those who wish to see wild lands and scenic resources preserved without dams and reservoirs, who want to see water reserved for purposes other than the irrigation of desert and the growth of cities, to gather in numbers in the proper places. They should hover in swarms over the Trinity and Marble Mountains wilderness, gather in clouds over Kings Canyon and the upper Kern. They cannot defeat the dam builders, nor should they want to do so, but they can make them change their course and detour around some sections of wild California. One thing is obvious. The men who control the water control the future of California. Nothing is more important to the West than water.

NINE

WHERE THE AIR
WAS CLEAR

Have we fallen into a mesmerized state that
makes us accept as inevitable that which is in-
ferior or detrimental, as though having lost
the will or the vision to demand that which is
good?   —RACHEL CARSON *

Nᴏᴛ long ago I went back for another look at Bodega
Bay. We had lunch in a quiet restaurant by the shore and
watched the gulls following the white breakers and the
fishing boats out on the horizon. It seemed quiet and pleasant, hardly a battleground. We looked over at Bodega
Head, a place that now means many conflicting things to
people. It is a rugged headland that meets the full brunt
of the Pacific waves and shelters the little harbor behind it.
Not far away the equally attractive Tomales Point shelters
the long, narrow reach of Tomales Bay. Near its mouth is
Dillon Beach, home of the Pacific Marine Station, the biological station of the University of the Pacific.

Because of the variety of intertidal habitats, Bodega
Head and its environs have long been a haunt for marine

* *Silent Spring.* Boston, Houghton Mifflin, 1962.

biologists. Those of us who have trained at the marine station have become intimately familiar with the rocks, coves, and sandy beaches of the area. Here, after long deliberation and search for suitable sites, the University of California decided to locate its new marine biological station. Just to the south is the Point Reyes National Seashore, one of the new gems in the crown of the National Park Service. Its unique coastline, varied vegetation, and animal life have been deemed worth preserving even though they lie in the area of high real-estate value just north of San Francisco Bay. The region around Bodega Head is a place of exceeding beauty that has attracted artists, naturalists, and others who simply admire wild scenery. Most of these people, from biologists to Sunday drivers, were shocked when they heard that a nuclear-power plant was being proposed for Bodega Head.

The growth of industry brings an increased demand for power. The growth of population, all of whom expect as their birthright a liberal supply of electrical appliances, brings an even greater demand. The state's ability to provide for this demand, even with all the high dams and hydroelectric stations, has been sorely taxed. New avenues for power production have had to be explored. One of the most promising seemed to be the exploitation of nuclear energy for the production of electric power. But nuclear-power plants have special requirements. Among other things they require large quantities of that scarce commodity, water. Fortunately, they can accommodate to salt water, of which there is plenty, but this means that to do so they must find space to locate along the ocean shore. Such space is at a premium. The first of the nuclear-power plants to be built on the seacoast in California, by the Pacific Gas and Electric Company, was on Humboldt Bay. Here it was possible to obtain an intake of water from a slough directly behind the plant, and to discharge the effluent water directly into Humboldt Bay. In the bay are major tides that serve to exchange and flush the water out into the sea. The land used was in an area already badly battered by untidy industrial development. It had little recreational potential. Few cared what happened to it. The discharge, although of warm water bearing some radioactive waste particles, was diluted so rapidly in the bay and ocean that no difficulties were foreseen, no objections raised, and no troubles have yet developed.

When the Pacific Gas and Electric Company sought a site for its second seacoast power plant, it encountered a different problem. An ideal site seemed to be Bodega Head, located north of San Francisco. Here they could draw water from the bay and discharge it into the ocean. The P.G. and E. planners gave the site a proper evaluation, and perhaps thought that they had considered all possible angles. I do not know if they foresaw any difficulty from the groups that are sometimes contemptuously called the "bugs and bunny people" or the "little old ladies in tennis shoes." Undoubtedly they thought that any of these could be ground underfoot without much trouble.

In 1961, when public hearings on the power plant were first held, the opponents of the P.G. and E. plan began to marshal their opposition. When this was loudly voiced, one might rationally expect that P.G. and E. would consider some different location. But that would reckon without the history of this utility company. It has a long history of fighting the conservationists. It has tackled the federal Bureau of Reclamation without any hesitation in its efforts to forestall the development of publicly owned hydroelectric power. It has fought off the state water planners

and the Department of Fish and Game. In the interest of
its stockholders' dividends, it has fought with the giants and
it was not going to pay attention to what were apparently
pygmies in the conservation field.

Initially it appeared that the conservation interests would
have the full fighting support not only of the usual conservation groups, led by the formidable Sierra Club, but
would also receive the backing of biological scientists
throughout the country. Unfortunately, however, those
who opposed the power plant misjudged the situation. Instead of fighting from the solid ground of defending aesthetic values and the scientific worth of one of the best
places for studying marine life, they decided to fight in the
boggy morass of radioactive contamination. Thus, at a time
when nuclear testing was a national issue, a straight-out
conservation fight became tangled up with the Cold War
and the Ban-the-Bomb movement.

The subject of radioactivity and the possibility of radioactive contamination endangering human and animal life
is one clouded with fear and confusion in the public mind.
The secrecy that surrounded the development of nuclear
weapons and that continues to surround the entire subject
of nuclear power has made it difficult for the average citi-
zen to obtain a clear picture of the problem. The spectacle
of conflict between giants of the scientific world—Robert
Oppenheimer versus Edward Teller, for example—has not
helped to ease public feeling. When a Nobel scientist dis-
agrees flatly with an official Atomic Energy Commission
statement on what should be a matter of scientific fact, the
man untrained in the mysteries of atomic physics can only
stand uneasily by. The government scientists, because of
security problems, cannot speak the whole truth. It is not
strange that there is room for public doubt that they are

speaking any of the truth. When we are told by the government that a certain concentration of Iodine 131, Strontium 90 or Cesium 137 is safe we could perhaps accept this as fact, if some nongovernment scientist did not promptly disagree with it, and if the government itself did not change positions from time to time. Besides, such terms as "maximum permissible concentration" make us wonder. "Permissible by whom?" Did we really authorize the government to give us a little poison, so long as it was not too much?

The public listened at first when the question of radioactive contamination of the marine environment was first raised at the Bodega Bay hearings. However, when scientists testified on both sides of the issue they began to doubt the validity of the statements made. Thus marine biologists of repute testified of the dangers of radioactive contamination, only to be contradicted by equally well known marine biologists on the other side. Both sides seemed authoritative and sincere, but one must have been wrong. The public could not readily judge. When some more extreme groups jumped into the fight and the whole subject of fallout from atomic weapons testing seemed to be getting mixed up in the issue, many conservation-minded people began to back away from the fight. It was not until the issue of radioactive contamination was thoroughly confused that another highly important issue was raised.

Bodega Head is located squarely on the San Andreas Fault. In a major earthquake it can be expected that part of the head will move northward relative to the other part and that there will be vertical shifts of some magnitude. While the proposed atomic plant does not sit squarely on the main fault line, it was found, belatedly, by geological consultants for P.G. and E. to sit at least on a subsidiary fault. At best it was a somewhat risky position for a major power plant. It brought to mind, at worst, the dangers of runaway atomic fission following a major earthquake. The earthquake question brought back into the fight some of the more conservative opposition to the power plant, including Secretary of the Interior Stewart Udall, the Lieutenant Governor of California, and the San Francisco Board of Supervisors. (The latter were told to keep their noses out of Sonoma County affairs by the Sonoma supervisors!) It might be expected that at this point along the line the Pacific Gas and Electric Company would have given way and looked for a different site. But they chose to fight to a finish. The finish came at last when the Atomic Energy Commission raised serious doubts about the safety of the plant in the event of a major earthquake. Finally, after investing many millions of dollars, P.G. and E. abandoned its plan for an atomic installation. In one final gesture, perhaps of defiance toward conservation interests, the company maintained that the possibility of constructing an unsightly non-nuclear electric plant on the site was still under consideration. However, late in 1964, complete abandonment of the project was announced and the area was made available for development as a park.

One could sacrifice a Bodega Head on the altar of industrial progress if only this one site, scenic and valuable though it may be, were involved. But instead it seemed that P.G. and E. and its relative, Southern California Edison, had no intention of stopping with Bodega Head. Other places of great scenic value on the California coast have also been nominated as sites for power stations. Already the battle lines have been drawn over a proposed plant to be built by the city of Los Angeles at Malibu Beach, and another nuclear plant proposed by

Southern California Edison for San Onofre, north of Oceanside in San Diego County. In all instances the power interests have simply ignored or attempted to override those who opposed them. There seems no spirit of compromise, no willingness to meet additional expense in order to preserve the goodwill of those who want to keep the natural beauty of the California coast.

It was inevitable that California should become a major industrial state. Starting from the necessity for supplying machinery for the mines, and supplied with an abundance of timber and other raw materials, California soon developed into a milling and manufacturing center for the West. In the 1860's, when California's great oil fields were first developed for kerosene production, it was forecast that the state would become one of the leading petroleum producers in the nation. Some decades later the San Joaquin Valley and Los Angeles coastal plain were to become studded with oil derricks, while refineries were to grow to produce the fuel needed for the burgeoning automobile industry. World War II gave the final push to industrial growth, with the location of the aircraft industries in Southern California. In the 1960's California rivals the eastern seaboard as an industrial center for the country.

The growth of industry, while making possible the prosperity that has attracted people to California, has also brought with it a deterioration of the environment in which people must live. While not approaching the deplorable conditions that accompanied the Industrial Revolution in Europe some centuries before, the problems of industrial pollution of the air, water, and land have been severe enough in California to demand an early solution. A copper smelter, installed without attention to the control of its poisonous waste products, can give off fumes that will destroy all life in the surrounding countryside. A cement factory can give off dust that coats the entire surrounding region and kills off all vegetation. A pulp mill or oil refinery can give off such foul odors that people for miles around will object to the smell, even when they do not consider the possible health hazard. A chemical factory, pouring its wastes into a nearby stream, can poison all of the aquatic life for miles downstream. Most industries that process raw materials have obnoxious or poisonous waste products that can either pollute the air, the water, or both. When these industries are few and far between, the pollution can be tolerated. When they become concentrated they create a threat to the total environment. Rarely do industries seem to control or contain their waste products until forced by public opinion and governmental regulation. Often this pressure is not forthcoming because the industries govern the economic prosperity of a community and influence its political life. A recent example from Northern California serves to illustrate this point.

With the decline of lumber manufacturing in Humboldt County following on the end of the Douglas-fir boom, it became apparent to many that the continued prosperity of the region depended upon diversification of the forest industries. There was, in particular, an abundance of raw materials suitable for the manufacture of pulp for paper, but no pulp mills were located in the area. In the 1950's the community acted to guarantee an adequate water supply to meet the extravagant needs of pulp manufacture. In the 1960's suitable sites were located, and both the Georgia-Pacific and Simpson companies announced their intention of constructing pulp mills in the Eureka area. Georgia-Pacific moved first, and planned a $30,000,000 installation, employing some hundreds of people. The local Chambers

of Commerce leaped with joy, and the newspapers head-
lined the news.

The problem of air pollution from pulp mills is known
to all who have lived near them. In addition the mills give
off vast quantities of waste water laden with potentially
toxic chemicals. It is possible to develop a mill that does
not give off such fumes, and one in which poisonous waste
products are recycled and not discharged into the surrounding rivers, bays, or ocean. However, such development
costs more and increases operating costs. Those who plan to
build up an industry seek out a community in which their
costs will be minimized. Always there is the unspoken
threat that if the community does not cooperate, the mill
will be located elsewhere. Such a threat can cause local
business and land interests to shiver. Thus, when the pulp-
mill issue came up before the City Council of Eureka there
were those who hoped earnestly that no one would say anything unpleasant that might offend the Georgia-Pacific
company. Someone did. The organization known as the
League of Women Voters is noted for asking embarrassing
questions before city councils and county supervisors. In
this instance spokesmen for the league pointed out that
there were no regulations on air-pollution control in the
area and suggested that an Air Pollution Control District
be set up to organize the necessary controls before the pulp
mill was constructed. The reaction of some of the city
councilmen was to be expected. One said, as quoted in the
Humboldt Standard: "If there's anything that's discouraging it's the little old lady in tennis shoes crying. Let's
wait and see what they are going to do, if they are going to
pollute the air. They are going to bring $30 million here;
we should be thankful to them. . . ." Another pointed out
hopefully that "pulp mills are not obnoxious any more."

Still another added, "If we are going to stop, we are not going to progress. . . ." Thus local pressures and consideration of the tax dollar can act to permit an industry to ruin living conditions in a community. Fortunately, action is being taken in Humboldt County. Whether or not it will be effective remains to be seen. Each day one can see a pall of smoke from the existing lumber mills hanging over the region, and a car left parked overnight will be covered with a fine layer of ash in the morning, but perhaps the pulp mills will not add to the problem.

The State of California has a Water Pollution Control Board that has in recent years taken highly effective action to prevent contamination of water supplies with waste products. But such control agencies can seldom act to stop water pollution. Instead they can only hope to minimize it and keep it within tolerable limits. They cannot keep us from being poisoned a little.

Industries are not alone in contaminating the environment. They are joined by communities that still pour raw sewage into streams, bays, or along ocean shores, and by the many more that allow detergent-laden wastes to foam out of the sewage disposal plants. More recently they have been joined in ever-growing numbers by agriculturalists who use poisonous dusts and sprays to kill off insects and other farm pests. Rachel Carson launched an effective attack against the latter group in particular by writing her book *Silent Spring*. But despite her efforts the poisoning goes on, and agricultural scientists who should know better have rallied in defense of the practice.

One of the more recent and distressing examples of pollution in California involves one of the most pricelessly scenic locations in the world, Lake Tahoe. Located at an elevation of over 6,000 feet in the Sierra Nevada, Tahoe is the largest mountain lake in the United States, formed by the combined operation of earthquake faulting and glacial action. It lies in a depression ringed by the high Sierra peaks, where pine and fir forests open into green mountain meadows, and was a clean blue trout lake, used in the past almost as a standard for clarity of fresh water. When I first knew it there were few people there—some Forest Service campgrounds, a ranger station, a few small communities, and some summer homes. After World War II, however, Tahoe suddenly became the fashionable place to go, where people wanted to be seen during the summer months. Homesites sprang up along broad stretches of shoreline. Unplanned rural housing tracts grew up in many locations. Next, the big gambling establishments from Reno and Las Vegas opened huge casinos to provide legalized gambling and nightclub entertainment on the California border. Ski lodges grew up in the vicinity to provide attraction for people, winter and summer. Finally, the Nevada gamblers began to build skyscraper hotels at the town of Stateline to atract even greater numbers of people to the area. Since it was virtually unplanned, these new developments had insufficient facilities for the disposal of sewage and wastes. Seepage and effluent from sewage-treatment plants began to pour in ever-greater quantities into the once clear Tahoe water. In 1963, as a result of a survey carried out by experts on sewage-disposal problems, it was pointed out that unless some answers could be found to prevent the discharge of sewage materials into the lake the entire nature of Lake Tahoe would be changed. Instead of a clear blue mountain lake it would become a green, algae-fouled cesspool. A survey by the federal Water Pollution Control Advisory Board carried out late in 1963 led to a warning to the states of Nevada and California that unless prompt action was taken it would be necessary for the United States to take legal steps to bring about abatement of the pollution. In October, 1963, agreement between the states was finally reached on a program for sewage disposal. While facilities for removing sewage from the lake basin were being constructed, it was agreed that a curb would be placed on further building within the area. Thus, after a serious pollution problem had been allowed to come into existence, and with the situation nearly critical, action was finally initiated by the pollution-control agencies involved.

One of the most critical pollution problems with which California has long been faced is that of severe air pollution. Los Angeles has become known as the city that made smog famous. The concentration of industries, smoking city dumps, backyard incinerators, chimney smoke from houses, and the fuming exhausts of millions of automobiles provide a major source for air pollution. Atmospheric conditions that create temperature inversions and permit stagnant air masses to hang over the city for long periods of time permit the buildup of the combination of pollutants and fog that became known as smog. It is ironic to think that the astronomical observatories on Mount Wilson and Palomar Mountain were attracted to the region because the air was clear, and that the clear, sunny summer days were a factor causing the movie industry to center at Hollywood rather than in the East. Anyone who flies in from over the deserts today and has to come down in a plane into the murky mess that overhangs Los Angeles can wonder why any community should tolerate such a situation. But the question has become, rather, What can the community do about the situation? Perhaps if industries had been required from the start to control the output of smoke and fumes, if the

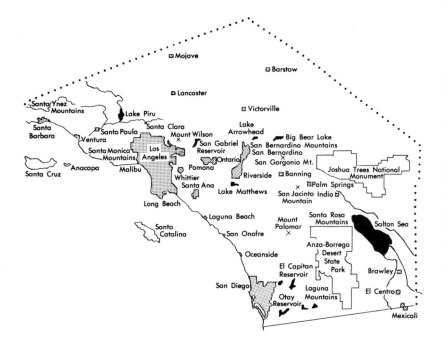

FIG. 19. Where things are in Southern California. The urban-industrial spread is even wider than can be shown by this location map.

concentrations of freeways and automobiles in the city had been prevented, if people had been kept from burning trash, the problem would not have developed, and it certainly would not have become severe. However, action against the condition did not occur until it had become almost intolerable, and by then it was extremely difficult to control. The communities of Southern California and the state government have tried valiantly to solve the problem. The most recent step is a state law requiring that all cars be equipped with devices that prevent the pouring of poisonous fumes from their exhaust pipes. However, the smog remains today, a menace to health, a source of discomfort for people, and of corrosion for installations and machinery. Los Angeles is not alone in the problem. Air pollution has become critical over most of the population centers of California, and in some of these even the first steps have not been taken to control it. We have reached the point where we no longer even hope to eliminate pollution, but only to keep it within "tolerable" limits where it does not cause acute discomfort or danger. We no longer think that pure air or clean water is our natural right. We accept our daily potion of poison as a price for civilization.

TEN

THE WEST
ENDS HERE

"Now, *here*, you see, it takes all the running
you can do, to keep in the same place. If you
want to get somewhere else, you must run at
least twice as fast as that!" —LEWIS CARROLL *

I HAVE a daughter who is just past ten years old. In California that makes her an old-timer. Six million people have arrived in the state more recently than she has. If she and her classmates in the fifth grade could comprehend what has happened to California since they were born, they would not only be old-timers; they would also be conservationists. It's that kind of state.

When I left California in 1941, there were approximately 7,000,000 people within its borders. When I was once more settled within the state in 1946, there were 9,000,000. Today there are 19,000,000. The California that I remembered from childhood had between 3,000,000 and 4,000,000 people. Thus in my lifetime there has been a sixfold increase. This is the most compelling reality of life in California—population increase unmatched in any other

* *Through the Looking-Glass.*

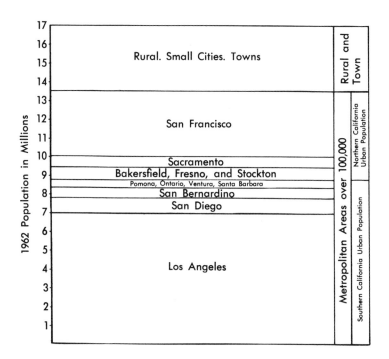

FIG. 20. Californians are city people. Eighty percent live in large metropolitan areas. The city dwellers of Southern California, more than half the state population, can decide the future of the entire state.

part of the United States—an overwhelming increase that has changed the state completely.

Today the state is adding more than 600,000 each year —adding a population equivalent to that of the city of San Diego each year. They all want housing, food, and water. They all hope to enjoy the state's beaches, its parks, its mountain ski lodges, its hunting and fishing. They all want jobs, schools, and the products of industry. They all consume electric power, burn gasoline, crowd the highways in cars. Small wonder that the state administration is forced to accomplish major miracles in every year—miracles in water development, highway construction, school building, facilities for industry. No state before had to plan for so many people coming all at once. Can the planners be blamed if the suburbs sprawl and the facilities become over-crowded? Each month you add a town of 50,000—each day you must accommodate more than 1,600 new people —each hour something must be done for the 70 people that have arrived in excess of those that have departed. Can this process continue? Can it be stopped? Most of the gain is from immigration. Most of the people settle in Southern California where there is less water, less space, less fresh air. If the present numerical increase continues, a decrease in the rate of increase, the population ten years hence, in 1975, will be 25,000,000. If the rate of increase stays the same as between 1950 and 1960, the population ten years hence will be close to 30,000,000. Perhaps some can regard these figures wih optimism and complacency. One who can remember California as it was can hardly feel that way.

Two hundred years ago the population of California consisted of some 130,000 Indians distributed over its 100,-000,000 acres of land. Each of them had more than a square mile of land to roam over, if the state were to be evenly divided among them. Actually, they were congre-gated in limited areas, essentially the same places where people live today. The high mountains, most of the dense forests, the open plains, and the deserts were avoided. People lived in what ecologists call "edge" situations, areas where vegetation types are interspersed. In such areas are the greatest number and variety of wild animals, and the greatest quantity of most kinds of food plants. Despite this tendency to congregate, there was no crowding. The In-dians had their difficult days, when drought came and food

failed, but for the most part their environment was benign
and friendly.

Undoubtedly the Indian population declined after the
Spanish arrived. The common ailments to which the Spanish were immune became death-dealing epidemics among
the natives. The change in customs forced by contact with
missions and pueblo made the Indians more susceptible to
disease. But the Spanish influenced only a small part of
California. Over most of the state life among the Indians
went on much as before. One hundred and twenty years
ago, in 1846, it has been estimated that there were 14,000
Spanish and somewhat under 100,000 Indians. The distribution of people had not changed much from precolonial
days. There was space to spare.

The Gold Rush brought people from everywhere. Most
settlers came from the American states; most were white.
But to provide help with the labor problem, great numbers
of Chinese were brought in. The new white settlers were
racially intolerant. The Indians were deliberately decimated. In 1850 there may have been 85,000 of them; by
1852 there were only 31,000 left. The Spanish-Mexican
people were disliked and distrusted. The Chinese, who
grew in numbers to 35,000 by 1860, were entirely too
hard working, too well able to save and accumulate wealth
to be liked. Enmity for them sprang up in particular among
the poor Irish immigrants who competed with them for
jobs. Racial violence and intolerance between national
groups marked the nineteenth century in California. One
hundred years ago, in 1865, the population of California
exceeded 400,000, and nearly one-fourth of these belonged
to the Chinese, Mexican, and Indian minority groups.
Nevertheless space was still plentiful, and most of the state
was empty. Concentrations of people were in the gold-camp

region of the Sierra foothills. The only city was San Francisco, but it was booming.

Between 1850 and 1870 the population of California
increased fivefold. Between 1870 and 1890 it more than
doubled again, standing in 1890 at more than 1,200,000.
A new urban center had grown at Los Angeles, one that
soon surpassed San Francisco in size. Other urban nuclei
were forming at San Diego and Sacramento. Space, however, was still no problem. There was an abundance of
land even though it had been badly used, and people could
feel the consequences of misuse when drought or flood hit
the countryside. The rate of population increase in these
early decades was remarkable, but the numerical growth
was not large and was readily absorbed.

From 1890 to 1910 the population once more came close
to doubling. From 1910 to 1930 it more than doubled, and
climbed to 5,700,000. These new increases, although at the
same rate as those earlier, were of a different magnitude,
millions of people instead of thousands. Difficulties were
encountered. Slums grew; unemployment became massive;
poorly placed farmlands were ruined and abandoned; forests and rangelands were damaged. Still the early pattern of
settlement could be bent and modified to take up the excess. Crowding had become a problem, but not to the extent that it seriously menaced the land itself. Had the
population growth curve followed the neat pattern that
demographers were using in the 1930's, had it leveled off
and stabilized, California would have remained one of the
most favored lands on earth.

But from 1930 to 1950 the population once more doubled, and by 1970 it will have doubled again. Five million
new people arrived by 1950; by 1970 an additional 10,-
000,000 will be added. The sheer mass of increase has

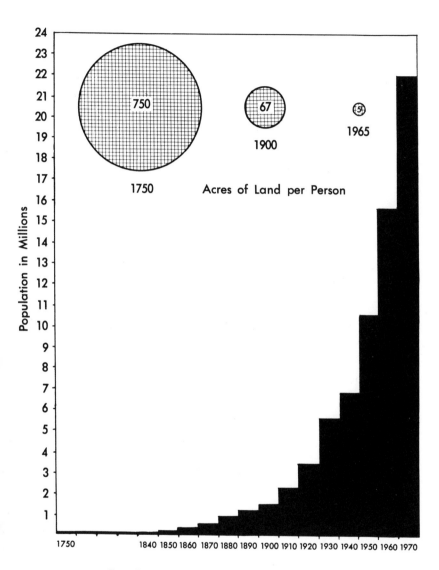

FIG. 21. Populations increase, and space available decreases, until today everyone feels the pressure. Note that although the rate of increase does not change much, the sheer bulk of population added after 1940 creates a new kind of problem, one requiring a massive reshaping of the natural environment.

created an entirely new problem. The old urban-industrial framework cannot accommodate it; the old communication, power, and water systems have broken down. To make room a massive redevelopment is taking place; the entire state is being reshaped. Since planning cannot keep up with growth, the reshaping is at times haphazard, and the results are generally undesirable. The old California no longer exists. The new is disturbing to contemplate.

One of the most serious consequences of the rapid population increase has been uncontrolled urban growth. Most of California's people are city dwellers. Most live in the San Francisco and Los Angeles metropolitan areas. Perhaps it is a mistake to call them city dwellers, since the urban areas have ceased to be cities and have become the sprawling, formless areas of urban congestion that Patrick Geddes once termed conurbations. A. E. Heller and S. E. Wood, writing of this problem, have called the new areas "slurbs." The name fits too well. The experience of San Francisco helps to illustrate the problem of city growth and decay.

It cannot be said that San Francisco was ever a planned city. It simply grew. What saved it from complete chaos was its fortunate geographic location on a hilly peninsula, and its necessary orientation toward the waterfront on the bay. The limits of the peninsula, like the walls of old cities in Europe, circumscribed its growth and forced its builders to face up to some limitations in space. The steepness of its hills forced some further organization upon its development. Although builders tried to ignore the hills and laid their gridirons of square blocks and rectangular lots over hill and valley alike, some hills were too steep and resistant to be so overrun. Thus, despite the indifference of its citizenry, San Francisco became a beautiful city, and because of the varied nature of its population it became necessarily a cosmopolitan city. It was always set apart from small-town uniformity and dullness.

San Francisco had its start in 1776 when Mission Dolores was founded, inland on the peninsula. Located on Mission Creek, near a small lake, it backed up against hills covered by coastal scrub and grass. The setting was attractive. Some miles away, fronting on the Golden Gate, a Presidio was built to guard the entrance to the harbor. No pueblo of consequence developed. When Richard Dana visited the area in the 1830's, San Francisco had lost out to its rival missions to the southward. Such trade as there was, mostly in hides and tallow, came through the ports of San Jose and Santa Clara, not from San Francisco. The United States took over the city in 1846 when its total population was less than 300. Two years later, in 1848, most of these departed as the rush to the goldfields began.

What was to be the city of San Francisco centered at first some miles from the Mission at the foot of Telegraph Hill. Here the first pier was built into the bay to accommodate the loading and unloading of ships. In 1849 and 1850 people by the thousands landed to head out for the goldfields. But many of them, seeing the opportunities for fleecing the miners, stayed instead to build up a city. Streets were laid out, after a fashion, and the first tents and then frame buildings went up. By 1849 the population had grown to more than 8,000 and the number of buildings to more than 500. It was, however, a city of men. The few women that were around were virtually worth their weight in gold dust. It was a city without sidewalks, where streets were thick with mud in the winter, and the unfortunate drunk who fell face downward could smother.

The growth of San Francisco came so fast that those who

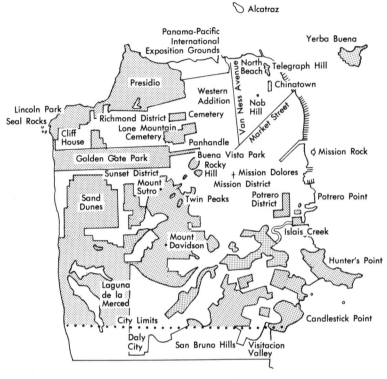

SAN FRANCISCO 1915

FIG. 22. San Francisco in 1915. Rebuilt after the fire and earthquake, the city invited the world to attend its Panama-Pacific International Exposition. The future pattern of urban growth was already determined, but at this time green spaces and open country (shown in the dotted pattern) dominated the southern and western parts of the city.

spent a half-year in the goldfields returned to find the place unrecognizable. There was much opportunity to undo early mistakes in building, since the city burned down every year in the first few years of growth. Gradually shacks and tents gave way to substantial buildings. Streets were paved, and public transportation was supplied. Water was brought in by developing local springs, artesian wells, and streams. By 1859, 100,000 people lived in San Francisco and it was one of the great cities of America—the only city in the West still largely inhabited by wild Indians. Almost from the start San Francisco became a manufacturing center, since the mines demanded machinery and equipment that could not be supplied from elsewhere. As money from the mines poured, in turn, into the city, it was to become a financial center where great fortunes were accumulated and used to control the affairs of the state. To its developing harbor came ships from all the world. As the area around the waterfront was taken over by trade and industry, housing for the working and middle classes pushed outward to the west and south. The wealthy took to the hills. The mansions belonging to Mark Hopkins, Leland Stanford, Flood, and Crocker grew on the heights to be known as Nob Hill, where they dominated the city skyline as their owners dominated the city's financial world. By the middle 1870's San Francisco had grown to a city of 250,000, and was equal in building style to any in the New World. There was an obvious lack of architectural unity, but a high degree of Victorian ostentation that is still to be observed in the older sections of the city. The bay window had appeared as a San Francisco institution, as had the practice of building houses almost or actually wall to wall, on narrow lots.

From early days the city began to center on Market Street, a "grand boulevard" laid out in the best style of the leading world capitals of the day, cutting diagonally across the grid of other streets. Market Street was dominated by the impressive Ferry Building at one end and aimed at the height of Twin Peaks at the other. Had there been consistent planning, the civic buildings and monuments that were to come would have faced on Market. But planning was little in evidence. The city grew too fast; its civic center grew up off Market, and the street was left as a broad avenue that served mostly to interfere with crosstown traffic.

By 1890 San Francisco had 300,000 people, while its nearest rival in the West, Los Angeles, was a struggling beginner with only 50,000 citizens. It had burst its old bonds set by the ring of hills fronting on the bay. A new residential area, the Western Addition, grew up beyond the hills, with pretentious Victorian buildings and architectural confusion, reaching out to the cemeteries of Lone Mountain. From the first nucleus on Nob Hill, the homes of the wealthy had extended northward to Russian Hill and had then followed the hills westward to the old Presidio, to look down from their remote splendor on the cluster of lesser houses sprawling out on lower ground.

Through some remarkable foresight the city fathers of 1870 established the boundaries of what was to be one of the great city parks of the world, Golden Gate Park. By 1890 its new superintendent, John McLaren, was busy changing the shape of the land inside the park boundaries, making forest and woodland, lake and glade where once were drifting dunes, planting wondrous groves of flowering shrubs and trees. At the other extreme, for those who preferred human vice to natural splendor, San Francisco offered in 1890 the wickedest spot in the world, the Barbary Coast, a concentration of brothels, dance halls, and gambling dens that had sprung up where the city had its beginnings below the slopes of Telegraph Hill. Regardless of inclination, or country of origin, anyone could find a home in San Francisco. Its Chinatown was world renowned, while colonies of Italians, Irish, Russians, Jews, and other national groups each had established its own district.

Mistakes made through lack of planning could have been rectified after 1906 when earthquake and fire virtually wiped out the downtown area. The newly constructed City Hall had collapsed in a pile of rubble; fires swept the homes of rich and poor. But the city that grew from the ashes followed the plan of the old city and served only to make it more permanent. In the decades that followed, up to World War II, the city grew further until somewhat more than 600,000 people lived there. In the twenties and thirties its last major area for expansion was filled in as the sand dunes of the Sunset district south of Golden Gate Park were leveled and paved over with continuous rows of boxlike houses, each with a lawn the size of a postage stamp in front and a rectangular yard behind. At the same time the truck gardens and pastures to the south were to spring up with similar houses and become the Sunnyside, Ingleside, and Potrero districts. These new areas were bedroom districts for people who worked and played downtown. They included no new community centers, no places of interest, only housing space, so many square feet per customer. Following World War II some small additional expansion was still possible, southward along the seacoast, and upward into the hills around Twin Peaks and Mount Davidson, hills that had formed a green belt separating old from new districts. However, by the middle thirties most of the available space within the city had been occupied. The changes that were yet to come involved shifts in population, tearing down and rebuilding within the space already occupied.

In 1939 San Francisco had reached the culmination of

an era that had started with the rebuilding of the city after the fire and earthquake. Out in the bay, in a glittering mass of lights, the Golden Gate International Exposition opened on its own Treasure Island artificially built up from the bay. The ferries plied back and forth from the Ferry Building, carrying the thousands of visitors who thronged to see the glories of the present and the mysteries of the future as they were displayed by business and industry. But on either side of the ferry routes to the south and northwest stood the new bridges across the bay and Golden Gate. These were soon to finish the ferries, and through tying the city closely to Contra Costa, Alameda, and Marin counties they were to expedite the process of change and disintegration in the city itself.

San Francisco in the late thirties was as glittering and colorful as at any time in its history. The pattern already established in 1890 was still obvious, but many surface features had changed. The old Barbary Coast was no more, but in its place Telegraph Hill and North Beach offered most forms of good or bad entertainment to the public. Here was San Francisco's Latin Quarter, its rival to Soho and Chelsea or to Greenwich Village. Next to it was the new Chinatown that had grown from the destruction of the old, lacking opium dens, more sedate, but still as colorful. Nob Hill supported luxury hotels and apartments in place of the old mansions. Russian Hill and Pacific Heights still held their quota of extreme wealth, but new centers had grown up farther out at Seacliff and St. Francis Wood. In the Western Addition the districts around Fillmore Street became a new international center, San Francisco's Harlem, with Jewish, Japanese, Negro, Philippine, and Russian sections. Farther out the Richmond and Sunset districts were the middle-class stronghold; and their two- or three-bedroom box houses were the nearest thing to a suburban life that most could afford.

But in the 1930's the seeds of urban disintegration had sprouted, and the 1940's were to see their rapid growth. The automobile had long been on the scene, but only Henry Ford's Model T made them available to middle-income groups. In the 1920's cars were common; in the 1930's every family felt it must own one, in the 1940's and 1950's the family without two felt impoverished. With the widespread availability of the motorcar, the shift to the suburbs on a mass scale began.

A desire to live away from the city while still working within it was not new. Indeed, it existed since the first city was formed. However, it had been a pleasure restricted to a wealthy minority who had long ago realized the advantage of a town house and a country house, or several of each. The wealthy left the city to seek privacy, quiet, freedom from social restriction, or the opportunity for contact with nature. These things their wealth could command in greater or lesser degree in the areas accessible to railroad lines. With automobiles available they could spread even farther, and still go up to the city when business demanded it. In the 1930's the upper middle classes followed the tracks of the wealthy and bought property in the wooded hills of the Peninsula, or, braving ferryboats and electric trains, moved to the oak-covered slopes of Marin and Contra Costa counties. Here they spent their leisure in the summer, commuting during working days. When winter rains and cold descended, they moved back to their city houses, only to go forth again on the sunny weekend. When World War II ended, however, many of these people no longer felt the need for a city house. Instead they built their rambling homes on extensive grounds within easy driving distance of the city. The bay bridges extended the area for colonization. Soon the business and professional groups were joined by all the young war veterans and their growing families. The middle class fled the city in a mass exodus, hoping to find a lawn, a garden, and a quiet street where children could grow in the open air. For no down payment and a G.I. loan the real-estate men and bankers were quick to help them in their search.

Suburban tracts sprang up in an ever-expanding outward surge from the former city limits, down the bay side of the peninsula and even into the former salt marshes, down the ocean side where gales howled in winter and the surf crashed on once-wild headlands, up through the dairy country of the Marin hills, blotting out the orchards of the Santa Clara Valley and the walnut groves of Contra Costa. Lacking wealth to command anything, the new suburbanites settled for what they could get, and what they could get was look-alike cheap houses, with a minimum of garden, and finally much less privacy than had been available in the city.

The war in the Pacific had brought its inevitable consequences to the chief Pacific seaport. San Francisco's population increased by a third over the war years. Military personnel, shipyard and war factory workers and their dependents were crowded into every available space. Cheesebox "temporary" housing sprang up in the remaining vacant spaces only to become distressingly permanent. Those who crowded in to work the war plants included groups that had been but sparingly represented before the war—Negroes and unskilled whites from the South bringing with them all the bitterness and racial antagonism of that strife-torn region. San Francisco's Fillmore district had been an open and friendly place in the 1930's where

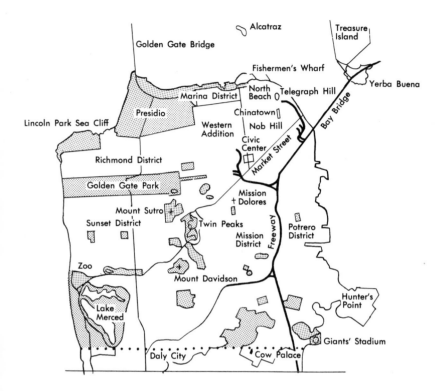

FIG. 23. San Francisco in 1963. Nearly fifty years of growth brought the blotting out of most green space and open country. Even the dead were moved from the old cemeteries to make way for the living. Extensive filling in of the bay created new land along the east shore. A system of freeways, still under construction, now slices through the city. Twin Peaks, once a symbol for the city, are now gouged by roads and almost covered by the spreading growth of housing.

anyone of any color could wander freely. After World War II, one hesitated to go there at night. By the 1960's, one hesitated to go there at all.

Back when the motorcar first appeared, John McLaren refused to allow them in Golden Gate Park. People laughed at his eccentricity, and public pressure finally forced him to change his ways. If the city authorities had had the wisdom and foresight, however, they would have followed McLaren's lead and refused to allow the automobile into the downtown area of the city. The first cars were noisy and quaint, and in their way attractive. They did not look, except to the unsophisticated, like the monsters they were to become. The liberty to drive where he pleased, extended to the early motorist, became license seized by hordes of drivers who were to come. People came to assume that their right to the "pursuit of happiness" guaranteed by the Constitution included in fine print the right to take their cars with them and find parking space wherever they might go in this pursuit.

With the mass exodus to the suburbs following on World War II came a daily mass movement of vehicles into and out of the center of the city. Each driver demanded parking space and each wanted to go and come his thirty, fifty, or seventy miles in time no greater than it used to take to come in from the Sunset district by streetcar. Surrendering to these demands, city and state authorities joined in destroying the city to make room for the motorcar. Where once office building, restaurant, or theater stood, new edifices grew, devoted exclusively to the storage of cars. Here one might have the pleasure of following a tight spiral road upward to park his car on a ten-story roof, or following it downward to park in a stall deep in the earth. Where once was housing or working space, new massive freeways, with their maddening approaches and exits, occupied the land. Those who sought to use the old city street system found themselves blocked off by freeway supports or, worse, forced up some freeway ramp and carried off in a mass of speeding vehicles to some unknown suburb. The old view down Market Street to the Ferry Building is gone, blocked off by a Bay Bridge ramp; the Civic Center is similarly obscured. The facilities for approaching or leaving the city continue to grow; the facilities for parking increase; the reasons for coming there at all continue to diminish.

Mass use of cars and emigration to the suburbs left the city in battered shape. The young families left for the doubtful joys of suburban life. The middle classes moved to distant sites. The poor and the old were left behind. Some districts, deserted by their former leavening of the wealthy, degenerated quickly into slums. The best districts did not change much; skid rows remained skid rows, but the in-between areas were hard hit. Not only did these deteriorate physically; they were taken over by underprivileged racial groups who could find no better place to live. All the strife between black and white that marks America in the 1960's is now to be found in San Francisco. In the 1930's I went to an integrated high school in the Western Addition, but nobody told me it was integrated. It contained black, brown, yellow, and white students. It also contained fat and skinny students. I don't remember any more significance being given to the color than to the shape. No students are so unsophisticated today.

Ever since the bloody days of the Barbary Coast, San Francisco has been swept periodically by waves of reform. Admittedly the ways of the Barbary boys were not bearable in a civilized community, but civic reform does not remedy human weakness. The city I grew up in had its red-light districts, its tenderloin, and skid row. It had its "tough" areas where you might be beaten or robbed. But these areas were known and could be avoided by those not looking for trouble. World War II brought a wave of reform under the peculiar illusion that the soldiers must be protected from vice. The known trouble centers were cleaned up, and their denizens consequently dispersed throughout the city. Where once if you avoided the known hazards you could walk anywhere in relative safety; now there are few places where you feel safe. Where the crowds are, while the crowds are there, you can move with confidence, but only then and there. The parks in particular, where children once played in safety, have become sources of danger. The people who might lead the fight to make the city once more safe for its citizens now get in cars and drive off to distant suburban homes or bury themselves in skyscraper apartments from which they cannot hear the troubles in the streets below. Deep in the suburbs among others of their own age and class they are removed from the sordid aspects of life, from seamy sex, ugly poverty, outrageous violence. There they can form receptive audiences for television programs that provide a glamorized version of the ugly things that still prevail in the old city.

San Francisco, like all cities, is being rebuilt. The city authorities are doing their best to clear slums, solve traffic problems, rebuild and reform the city while preserving some of its old charm and glamour. But the job is difficult, and can be successful only if some stabilization can be achieved, if the wave of influx of people and automobiles can be controlled, and if life can be pumped once more into the downtown heart of San Francisco.

The greatest reality in California today is the population problem. It touches on every facet of the land and its life, from the conservation of wilderness and national parks to the restoration of meaning and pleasure to life in the cities. Unless the rate of population increase can be checked and slowed to a point where planning can overtake it, there can be no good answer, only stopgap emergency measures for preserving the landscape and making life bearable in this once-golden state.

ELEVEN

ONCE THERE WAS A PLACE
CALLED CALIFORNIA

Sometimes it is necessary for men to scream
against a world they never made, and cannot
control.   —T. R. FEHRENBACH *

I KNOW a girl who maintains that her whole life has been
haunted by the vision of a place called Cherry Street. It
is a dreamland, she says, formed from reading too many
public school books about Dick, Jane, Sally, and their like.
In their world everybody is always pleasant and kind. They
all live in nice houses with friendly neighbors. There is no
trouble or violence, no social nastiness or antagonistic co-
operation, no race problems or wars. My own equivalent is
a place called California. Once I thought that I lived there.
Now I know it no longer exists, and suspect that it was
always a dream. Perhaps it resulted from staring too long
at the waves breaking on the coast, and thinking back, as
the song goes, "on all the tales you can remember—of
Camelot." Yet, at some times in some places I still feel
this place called California around me, but the times come
more seldom and the places are farther apart. More do I

* *This Kind of War*. New York, Macmillan, 1963.

wonder, nowadays, if such a world can be created by man. The practically minded tell me No. But the "roots of heaven" reach into men's hearts, and one must dream. Is it really too much to ask people to be concerned with the land in which they live? Is it too much to ask them to question those measures that come before city council or state legislature in the light of what effects they will have on their land? The dams on the Trinity are their concern. They will not only change the Trinity; they will bring more people to Southern California and irrigate more desert land. Perhaps some people think there are enough people in Southern California, and like to see deserts as deserts. If so, they had better watch the Trinity. The freeways that threaten to cut the heart out of San Francisco and destroy areas that all of us once thought were loved, cherished, and safe are surely everyone's concern, even if most people rarely visit the cities or places involved. The power of the State Highway Commission to condemn land can be curtailed if the people want it. Is it more important to "get there fast" or to have some place worth going to?

There are many areas in California that are underpopulated, just as there are those that are seriously overpopulated. With underpopulation the social amenities are lacking and cultural advantages are absent, even though wild land resources are abundant. With adequate planning it is possible to increase the population, to gain the cultural and social advantages, and still to preserve the wild country. It is everyone's concern to see that this is done, rather than have people continue to pile up in unsuitable locations.

Conservation is everybody's business. But what goes under that name today is often a piecemeal, stopgap activity that is often too late, and usually too little. It stands too often in the path of what is called progress, and thus arouses the ire of those concerned with moneymaking. Conservationists find themselves always in the desperate position of trying to impose some control over an activity that is already under way, or of trying to save some piece of land or scenery against the opposition of powerful pressure groups. Always their activities seem beside the point to those involved in the main business of our society.

A newspaper such as the *San Francisco Chronicle,* which has featured conservation news and played a role in the fight to preserve natural beauty in California, still must devote 90 percent of its news space to items that are at best only tangentially related to conservation. Is it that people are not interested in their environment and do not care much about conservation matters? The answer is obviously No. Too many people visit state and national parks, hunt or fish in national forests, join organizations dedicated to civic improvement, for one to say that they lack interest. Yet conservation often seems to lack urgency, to be peripheral to the main business of life. A crisis in Vietnam drives the most pressing conservation problems from the paper. The prospect of world destruction through nuclear war, stemming from the acceptance of an insane outlook on international affairs, can always drive matters concerning world improvement from the headlines. The exploration of outer space, a scientific exercise that seems to hold little relevance to our earthly problems, also captures headlines because of its relation to missilery, weapons, and international conflicts. We don't really want to spend billions for a handful of moon dust, only to see that the Russians don't grab it first. Basically the world crises that compel our attention are related to natural resource and population problems. Well-fed, well-clothed people who are integrated with their physical and social environment don't normally threaten their neighbors. Racial violence and unrest at home drive even international crises from the news. Again a basis can be found in conservation matters. A properly planned city with adequate opportunity for all would not breed the strife and turmoil that emanates from a Harlem or a Fillmore district.

My definition of conservation includes the ecology of man's environment and the social organizations that he uses to achieve a state of well-being within that environment. Conservation problems thus range from city organization to the preservation of wilderness areas. To me they cannot be dissociated. We cannot save a wilderness or a wild species without paying attention to the problems of life in the cities; we cannot have a satisfactory life in a city without having wild country and wildlife accessible on the horizon. We cannot plan for land and resources without consideration of human population problems. In California today, conservation problems, as so defined, are paramount.

The critical problem in California today is that of population increase. This is also the most important problem in the world today, but the California problem has a different aspect. The state is not threatened so much by a runaway birthrate, although this is involved, as it is by a runaway immigration rate. Birthrates have been declining in recent years. The use of new contraceptive chemicals and devices, and the widespread public awareness of population problems, have shown signs of bringing birthrates, as such, under control. But how, in a democratic society, can you prevent people from moving to the place where they want to live? We cannot insist upon a passport and visa for prospective visitors to California.

There are various answers to the problem of controlling population increase in California. One is relatively simple,

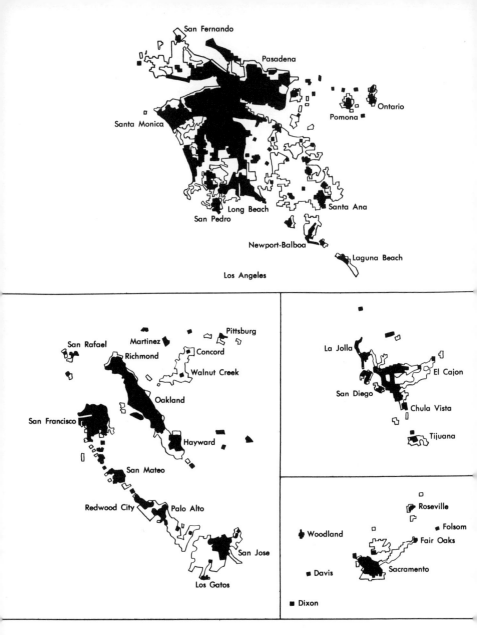

FIG. 24. The urban explosion. City limits in 1948 are defined in solid black; in 1964 they include the area inside the outer line. Roughly fifteen years of growth are shown, and the process is now accelerating.

and involves *not* planning for population growth. This means not encouraging new industries to move into an area. It means not developing our water resources to a maximum, and thus not providing the water that would make possible additional urban or industrial growth, or bring into production new farming areas. It means not building those new power stations or those new freeways. No real-estate development will be built in an area where electricity and water will not be provided. No industry will come where it will not receive space, power, or water. People will not come where there are no new jobs or new housing, or if they do come they will not stay. Immigration is not excluded, but the immigrants will be a minority willing to compete for existing jobs and housing space.

The idea of controlling population increase by not providing for it, and indeed forbidding the development of new facilities, is not original. It has been used already, on a small scale. One of the most charming places in California is the city of Santa Barbara. It has maintained its quiet beauty by excluding the kind of industrial growth that other cities have welcomed. It has not allowed housing sprawl. It has fought the State Highway Commission and its monstrous freeway system to a halt, temporarily at least. The continuing charm of the Carmel region, farther north, has been maintained by a firm and definite stand against "progress" by its residents. But these are small places, inhabited by the wealthy. It is most unlikely that active discouragement of population increase on a statewide scale will be tried out. It goes against the entire philosophy of the expanding economy. Too many people look forward to population growth, even while they decry its effects, for them to accept a plan for its discouragement. Such a plan would mean that all those who had invested in land would find land values no longer increasing. It would say to those in business and industry that they could expect no further expansion of the California market. All of us are too used to being pushed to higher levels by people crowding in from below to accept the idea that growth and expansion have ended.

Because the solution of conservation problems demands a rejection of the expanding-economy concept, most people will have ambiguous attitudes toward conservation issues. Many people will vote for a national park because only a few will have invested in the lands or resources to be included within that park. Those that have such investments may oppose that particular park, although they may be advocates of parks in general. Hardly anyone wants to see a nuclear-power plant on a scenic headland, but too many people own stocks in the power company, own land that can be increased in value when more power becomes available, or have shares in industries that require more power, for the opposition to its construction to gain an easy victory. I may favor a lessened rate of utilization of forest resources, but would howl loudly if my book could not be published because of a shortage of paper. Thus, although I am inclined to favor a Redwood National Park I sympathize deeply with Arcata Redwood Company, whose lands are involved. Support for conservation measures is therefore erratic, and the curtailment of population growth necessary to reach a real solution for our problems is generally inacceptable. Our very economic system prevents our doing the things needed to protect our environment from destruction, and we are sadly aware that other alternative economic systems in existence today work no better.

However, since we are facing this problem it is not fair to avoid looking at the whole picture. What is the alterna-

tive to our failure to curtail population growth? We must
then plan for population increase and work with all our
ability to provide for it. We must harness all available
power, develop all available water resources, utilize forests,
range, and farmland to a maximum, use more and more
land for housing developments. We must look forward to
a monstrous supercity extending from San Diego to the
Tehachapis and slopping over into the deserts, and another
one extending from the Sierra foothills to San Francisco's
peninsula, and reaching northward into the Sonoma and
Napa valleys, and southward to Carmel. But perhaps before these are fully developed we will begin to run out of
some essential. Water is the most likely to run short, even
with seawater conversion. No matter how much ingenuity
and technological skill we employ, some resource is going
to run out and prevent further development. When this
happens—and it may come fairly soon—we shall have
then reached the absolute limits of possible growth. We
must then face up to the problems that were evaded earlier.
The expanding economy can then expand no more; populations can grow no further; and a way must be found for
reorganizing and living with existing numbers within existing means. But, by then, what a wretched place California
will be!

It seems somehow more realistic to recognize now the
limits of growth and take measures to adjust to them. Is
it not more reasonable to slow down now, and not go full
speed ahead until we hit the stone wall that must inevitably
stop us? It is perhaps not reasonable to attempt to stop
population growth all at once, but it is unreasonable to do
nothing about it. Instead, while we still have wild mountains and forests, rangelands and deserts, scenic vistas of
parks and reserves, wild animals and space for free people,

we should start putting the brakes on further expansion. We can do it by not channeling those last wild rivers, by not building those extra power plants, by not issuing building permits for all those new suburbs. There are many effective ways that growth can be slowed, that massive immigration can be discouraged, that will not disrupt the economy of the state. Finding these ways and putting them into effect should be the job of state and local governments, and should underly all the regional planning that is going on today.

Whether or not we accept the curtailment of population growth as a primary goal, we must continue to do something about the other subsidiary conservation problems. The most urgent of these is the reorganization of the cities. Since most of California's people are city people, these areas must be tackled first if any order is to be achieved in the state as a whole. Like most people who are supporters of wilderness and wild country, I spend far more time in cities than I do in wilderness. Unlike most of my fellow wild-land ecologists, I like cities, particularly the big ones. Anyone who has read this far realizes my feelings toward San Francisco. I am sorry that I cannot like Los Angeles, but it is too formless and sprawling, rather like the San Francisco Bay area with the city of San Francisco removed. I am captivated by some of its environs. At Laguna Beach and Malibu, in Newport-Balboa and in the Palos Verdes development it has some of the most exceedingly beautiful living areas in the world. But behind these pleasant communities sits the vast ugly mass of disorganized industrial development around Wilmington and into Long Beach, the squalor of the decaying Venice region, the pressure of millions of people and cars, the snarl and confusion of the freeways. San Diego, by contrast, is a city where the physical setting has encouraged the development of unusually charming places to live, and the sheer mass of the city is not so great as to defy orderly planning. Through careful control of future growth and redevelopment it could lead all other California cities in urban beauty. The valley cities have always seemed wretched places to me, and I have resented every visit to the formless confusion that marks Sacramento, and the heat-deadened dullness of Fresno and Bakersfield. But these cities, in recent years, have been striving toward urban beauty. Fresno has reshaped its downtown area and has taken the courageous step of excluding the automobile from its central area.

At one time, writing in *Environmental Conservation*, I favored the idea that city and countryside must be made to flow together, in order to preserve the advantages of both. However, since visiting the cities of Europe, and doing some further reading and thinking on the subject, I have been inclined to change this viewpoint. L. Dudley Stamp, in his book *Applied Geography*, helps to focus thinking on this subject. Lewis Mumford, in his monumental work *The City in History*, provides more substance. Most confirmed urbanites like cities because they are distinct and different from village, small town, or rural area. They provide the happy anonymity and sense of freedom that comes from *not* knowing your neighbor. They have the rush and confusion that comes from diverse people purposefully pursuing their varied activities. They provide long nights when the lights sparkle and the sidewalks are not rolled up. They allow the activities and groups that can spring up only when populations begin to number in hundreds of thousands and members of minorities can come together in sufficient numbers to bolster one another. Parks and green places remain an essential part of all worthwhile cities, but too much integration of city and country can destroy the advantages of both.

I could not begin to plan a city, let alone one that would preserve those qualities of life that are essential to urbanity. But I hope that those now engaged in tearing down and rebuilding the cities of California will have these qualities in mind. Unfortunately, I see too much evidence that they are not being considered. The remolding of our cities to accommodate the freeway and the parking lot, the capitulation to the demands of the automobile, can destroy the integrity of any city. The central city at least should be built to the scale of a man traveling on foot. The central portions of London, Paris, Rome, and New York invite exploration on foot. I did not feel the need for a motorcar in Europe's cities, but the moment I reached California once more I felt stranded without one.

It is cheering to hear that a new "return to the city" is under way and that the great exodus to the suburbs may be at an end. However, such a move places a greater responsibility on the city authorities to control the mass of new construction that has already been begun. One hopes that a situation can be achieved such as has been approached in London, where a high percentage of people both live and work within a single borough or district of the city. In particular it would be well to see residential buildings going up on some of the downtown city sections. By locating hotels and apartments, restaurants and clubs in such areas, they can be kept alive at night. Today there are large sections of the central city that teem with people in the daylight, but die after dark. Location of living and playing space in such areas would further cut down on the need for transportation through the cities. The development of adequate, rapid public transportation systems could save the central city from the automobile blight. That this is needed is obvious to all, and it is discouraging to see further development of misplaced freeways using funds that could as well go to a more sensible transportation network.

The necessity for controlling the suburban sprawl has attracted the attention of most people, and is exercising the minds of all concerned with regional planning. It is not practical to eliminate the existing suburbs, but it is possible to organize them into urban centers distinct and separate from the original cities that spawned them. Most particularly we need to set bounds on further suburban development, protecting our high-quality farming lands from additional encroachment. The development of new urban centers within present suburban areas can allow for internal expansion of residential space and further cut down on the need for commuting to some distant center for work. This process, fortunately, is already at work in California; although the continuing spread of suburbs does still go on. Strict county zoning laws are badly needed to prevent the spreading growth of the ugly urban fringe areas that surround and connect both city and suburb . . . the area of billboard and junkyard, used-car lot and shacktown that makes the approach to any city discouraging.

It is easy to write these things, and my repetition of them here simply adds to the volumes of words already written. It seems incredibly difficult to put them into operation, even when the need is obvious. The small entrepreneur who wants to build his pizza parlor, fruit stand, or used-car lot in the orange groves outside the city limits still seems to have undue support from the county authorities. One of my friends, for example, has just waged a three-year fight to prevent the establishment of a crowded trailer park in what had been a first-class residential suburb. After endless hearings and legal wrangles, he lost the struggle, even though one would expect that any rational system of zoning would have supported his point of view. There are those who wish to maintain the right to exploit for a profit regardless of public interest. They still have authority. Those who would fight them fail to attract the support of fellow citizens who live in one place, work someplace else, play in a third place, and feel no community responsibility toward any of the areas concerned. Our dispersed way of living does not lead to the development of interest or pride in a single community. It is to the interest of the quick-profit developers to keep such pride in place from growing.

Moving away from city and suburb, a principal problem for California remains that of transportation facilities. Crowded two-lane highways give way to freeways that eat into farm and forest, towns and parks. Soon the freeways in turn are crowded, and traffic slows to a crawl. We build larger freeways, while population grows and more people buy more cars. More land is destroyed; the new superhighway is again crowded; and a new cycle of enlargement and land destruction begins. In desperation more and more people take to the air, and the growth of airfields encroaches on still more land. The problem of getting from airport to destination becomes as great as that of driving the entire distance to begin with. Meanwhile alternate forms of transportation are neglected. Railroads, which were far less space consuming than highways, fall into neglect, routes are abandoned, and service becomes infrequent. Yet, if attention were given to the problem, a fast, efficient, and comfortable system of rail transportation could surely be devised, and would cost less than the million dollars a mile we are pouring into new freeways. Yet we go on spending hundreds of millions on highway development, building a choking network of automobile roads. Admittedly the people, through their legislatures, have approved it. But did they know what they were approving? Were they offered any reasonable alternative? Most Americans like automobiles, but all have an inner feeling that driving them should be a pleasure. In California, pleasure driving is becoming an activity to be read about in history books, not a possibility for today.

The problems of California rural lands and wild country, apart from those imposed by urban sprawl and highway encroachment, are largely those of conflicting demands for an ever-shrinking quantity of space and for the water that can make that space usable. As a small, but highly important, segment of these problems are those related to parks and reserves, wilderness and wildlife. Like Morel and his supporters in Romain Gary's *The Roots of Heaven*, I believe that wild animal life and wild country is a bulwark of, and essential to, human freedom. So long as we have space where the wild game herds can wander undisturbed, we have a margin in which individual liberty can thrive. When we chain and confine all our wild country, eliminate the free-roaming animal life, then there will be no space left for that last wild thing, the free human spirit. The machine civilization we have built will have triumphed over us, and we shall have become mere numbers to be organized and moved about by computers. Aldo Leopold once wrote: "I am glad I shall never be young without wild country to be young in. Of what avail are forty freedoms without a blank spot on the map?" * There are no blank spots on the California map, but there is still wild country. If it goes, much of meaning of the word "human-

* *A Sand County Almanac* (New York, Oxford University Press, 1949).

ity" will go with it. We shall need a new word for the confined creatures that take the place of free men.

At a recent meeting on conservation problems, a resource economist described the necessity for putting a price tag on wildlife and wild country. If wildlife is to maintain a place in competition for land and water we must know its economic value, what the public will pay in order to keep it. He suggested that a step toward achieving this end would be an increase in the cost of hunting and fishing licenses, and presumably also of the fees for access to private lands for hunting and fishing. By such an increase we could get a better measurement of the value attached to our wildlife resources, and could use these figures in bargaining for such things as an allotment of water for a duck marsh or the reservation of lands for public hunting and fishing. While I agree that we need better measurements in economic terms of the values of wild land and wildlife, and have done some work toward attaining such measurements, I cannot agree that current price tags would be a true measure of worth to society. The value of a previously unexploited raw material—uranium ore is an example—cannot be known until its usefulness to society has been demonstrated. A realistic price for a new kind of manufactured product often cannot be set until a public demand for it has become established, usually through advertising its qualities. We cannot establish the value of a remote wilderness area, known to very few people, by determining the price that people will pay today to maintain it. People who know little about wild nature—and city people often have little opportunity to learn—cannot be expected to pay a high price for its maintenance. Yet, unless it is maintained, their understanding will come too late. Like the American Indians, they will have given away gold in exchange for glass beads. Aldo Leopold, in his *A Sand County Almanac,* touched on this problem years ago, saying that rather than building roads into the wilderness, we should be building new pathways of understanding into the still unlovely human mind. Such pathways are being built today. In a year of politics and crises, we can still have a wilderness-preservation bill enacted by Congress. But it is still too early to defend priceless aesthetic resources, reservoirs of human freedom, entirely in economic terms. Even highway engineers and water developers must be made to recognize that.

It is possible to stop, here in the West, the destruction of the land that is called California. It is not only possible; it is essential to do so. Ten years hence we shall regret every mistake we are making today, feel deeply the hurt caused by each failure to act. Admittedly we are trying hard to remedy past damage and prevent future loss. Few areas have so many planning agencies as California. Few have so many public and private organizations devoted to the maintenance of the wild scene and natural beauty of their country. Yet there is continuing failure and confusion. Some lack of integration in our efforts seems apparent. The pressures of economic growth and population sweep over the little plans of those who are seeking to preserve some space or enhance some natural beauty. The city planners seem to strive in vain against those whose activities would destroy the integrity of the city. Those building a state park system seem to operate in ignorance of the plans of other agencies that would destroy it. We cannot afford to have the various organizations and groups engaged in either preservation or development working in isolation from one another. The kind of wrangle that has gone on for years over Bodega Head or that threatens to go on over the state's Prairie Creek Redwood Park reflects some failure to get the interested groups together at an early enough stage. A long-term answer to the problem of California can come only through full consideration of the total environment within the state. From cities to wilderness plans must be coordinated.

The future of California actually rests in the hands of a relatively small number of groups of people that are involved in the protection of its resources or in their development or exploitation for profit. Half of the land is in federal or state control. Two agencies, the United States Forest Service and the Bureau of Land Management, exercise the major control and bear the greatest responsibility for the future of these areas. The other half of the land is in private hands. Here the lumber companies, the livestock owners, the farmers, and the real-estate developers are the groups in whose hands the future rests. Over these privately owned lands the various governments, town, city, county, and state, can exercise varying degrees of control. The state, particularly through its natural-resources agency that includes the Department of Water Resources, and through its Highway Commission, can exert the most important influence on all private activities, and therefore bears the greatest responsibility for future trends.

Of the various private groups, I believe that the lumber companies, much maligned though they may be, have been the most conservation-minded, in the broad sense of the word. I feel also that the real-estate developers, although some have been exemplary in their activities, have been the least responsive to the public interest. More research is obviously needed, if these private groups are to do an adequate job, and much of this must be sponsored by public agencies. We need further knowledge of forest and range management to make possible a more responsible use of these lands. We need much more work on the problems of agricultural pest control, to prevent the poisoning of our environment through pesticides. We need more work on economic means for the disposal of the waste products of industries and cities, to avoid further pollution of water and air. More government control is still needed to prevent permanent damage to the land by those groups that still seek a quick profit at the expense of the public welfare.

Fortunately, the very population pressure that threatens to destroy California has set in motion counterforces of conservation that can save it. Most of all we need a vision, an ideal, of what the state can be—a land that would permit the greatest diversity of human activities and the fullest expression of human freedom in a setting of natural splendor and man-made beauty—a place where technology is made to work for the interests of humanity, and man is not forced into a warped mold to suit the requirements of the computer. California can be a model that all the world would admire. It can set an example that all other regions will try to follow. But unless we act now to stop the forces of destruction that are at work, the state that once was green and golden may become an object lesson that shows only what other areas must avoid.

Principal References

ALBERTSON, F. W., G. W. TOMANEK, and A. RIEGEL. 1957. Ecology of drought cycles and grazing intensity of grasslands of the central Great Plains. *Ecological Monographs*, 27: 27–44.

AUDUBON, J. J., and J. BACHMAN. 1854. *The quadrupeds of North America*. V. G. Audubon, New York, 3 vols.

BARI, VALESKA. 1931. *The course of empire*. Coward-McCann, Inc., New York.

BEETLE, ALAN A. 1947. Distribution of the native grasses of California. *Hilgardia*, 17: 209–357.

BOLTON, H. E. 1911. Expedition to San Francisco Bay in 1770. Diary of Pedro Fages. Univ. Calif. Publ., Academy of Pacific Coast History, 2: 143–159.

———. 1930. *Anza's California expeditions*. Vol. I, *An outpost of empire*. Univ. Calif. Press, Berkeley.

BROOKS, C. E. P. 1949. *Climate through the ages*. Ernest Benn, London.

BROWN, HARRISON. 1954. *The challenge of man's future*. Viking Press, New York.

BRYANT, EDWIN. 1936. *What I saw in California*. Fine Arts Press, Santa Ana, Calif.

BUNNELL, L. H. 1911. *Discovery of the Yosemite and the Indian War of 1851 which led to that event*. 4th ed. G. W. Gerlicher, Los Angeles.

BURCHAM, L. T. 1957. *California range land*. Calif. Division of Forestry, Sacramento.

CAMP, CHARLES L. 1952. *Earth song*. Univ. Calif. Press, Berkeley.

CARR, JAMES K. 1963. Can California's beauty be kept? Santa Barbara *News Press*, March 3.

CARSON, RACHEL. 1962. *Silent spring*. Houghton Mifflin, Boston.

CARSTENSEN, VERNON, Editor. 1963. *The public lands*. Univ. Wisc. Press, Madison.

CHALFANT, W. A. 1922. *The story of Inyo*. W. A. Chalfant, Chicago.

CLAR, C. RAYMOND. 1959. *California government and forestry*. Calif. Div. of Forestry, Sacramento.

CLARKE, A. B. 1852. *Travels in Mexico and California*. Wright and Hasty's Steam Press, Boston.

CLELAND, ROBERT G. 1959. *From wilderness to empire*. Alfred A. Knopf, New York.

COY, OWEN C. 1929. *The Humboldt Bay region, 1850–1875*. Calif. State Historical Soc., Los Angeles.

CRONISE, TITUS FEY. 1868. *The natural wealth of California*. H. H. Bancroft, San Francisco.

DALE, E. E. 1930. *The range cattle industry*. Univ. Okla. Press, Norman, Okla.

DALE, H. C. 1941. *The Ashley-Smith exploration and the discovery of a central route to the Pacific, 1822–1829*. Arthur Clark, Glendale, Calif.

DANA, RICHARD HENRY, JR. 1949. *Two years before the mast*. Doubleday, New York.

DANA, SAMUEL TRASK. 1956. *Forest and range policy*. McGraw-Hill, New York.

———, and Myron Krueger. 1958. *California lands*. American Forestry Assoc., Washington.

DASMANN, RAYMOND F. 1959. *Environmental conservation*. John Wiley, New York.

DASMANN, WILLIAM P. 1959. *Big game of California*. Calif. Dept. of Fish and Game, Sacramento.

DAVY, JOSEPH BURTT. 1902. *Stock ranges of northwestern California*. U. S. Bureau of Plant Industry Bull. 12.

DEPARTMENT OF WATER RESOURCES. 1956–58. *Progress reports*. Calif. State Printing Office, Sacramento.

———. 1958. *Water facts for Californians*. Calif. State Printing Office, Sacramento.

DE ROOS, ROBERT. 1948. *The thirsty land*. Stanford Univ. Press, Stanford.

DOLDER, E. F. 1954. Water—California's lifeblood. *Conservation—concern for tomorrow*. Calif. State Dept. of Education Bull. 23: 45–63.

DOWNEY, SHERIDAN. 1947. *They would rule the valley*. Privately printed, San Francisco.

DUNHAM, H. WARREN, Editor. 1957. *The city in mid-century*. Wayne State Univ. Press, Detroit.

DYKSTERHUIS, E. J. Condition and management of range land based on quantitative ecology. *Jour. Range Management*, 2: 104–115.

ELLIS, CECIL B. 1954. *Fresh water from the ocean*. The Conservation Foundation. Ronald Press, New York.

FARQUHAR, FRANCIS P. 1933. *The topographical reports of Lieutenant George H. Derby*. Spec. Publ. No. 6, Calif. Historical Society, San Francisco.

———. 1949. *Up and down California in 1860–1864. The Journal of William H. Brewer*. Univ. Calif. Press, Berkeley.

FEDERAL WRITERS' PROJECT. 1939. *California—a guide to the Golden State*. Works Progress Administration. Hastings House, New York.

———. 1940. *San Francisco*. Works Progress Administration. Hastings House, New York.

FEHRENBACH, T. R. 1963. *This kind of war*. Macmillan, New York.

FLINT, RICHARD FOSTER. 1947. *Glacial geology and the Pleistocene epoch*. John Wiley, New York.

———, and E. S. Deevey, Jr. 1951. Radiocarbon dating of late-Pleistocene events. *Amer. Jour. Science*, 249: 257–300.

GARY, ROMAIN. 1958. *The roots of heaven*. Simon and Schuster, New York.

GILLIAM, HAROLD. 1963. This World, *San Francisco Chronicle*, Dec. 15.

GREGOR, HOWARD F. 1963. Spatial disharmonies in California population growth. *Geographical Review*, 53: 100–122.

GRINNELL, JOSEPH, J. DIXON and J. LINSDALE. 1937. *Fur-bearing mammals of California*. Univ. Calif. Press, Berkeley, 2 vols.

HARDING, S. T. 1960. *Water in California*. Palo Alto, Calif.

HEALD, WELDON F. 1949. Sierra snows, past and future. Sierra Club Bull. 34: 55–68.

HENDRY, GEORGE W. 1931. The adobe brick as an historical source. *Agric. Hist.* 4: 110–127.

HEIZER, R. F., and M. A. WHIPPLE. 1951. *The California Indians.* Univ. Calif. Press, Berkeley.

HIBBEN, FRANK C. 1960. *Digging up America.* Hill and Wang, New York.

HIGBEE, EDWARD. 1957. *The American oasis.* The Conservation Foundation, Alfred A. Knopf, New York.

HILLINGER, CHARLES. 1958. *The California islands.* Academy Publishers, Los Angeles, Calif.

HITTELL, THEODORE H. 1911. *The adventures of James Capen Adams.* Scribner's, New York.

Humboldt Standard, Nov. 20, 1963, Eureka, Calif.

HUTCHINSON, W. I. 1956. *Water for millions.* United States Forest Service, San Francisco, Calif.

HUTCHISON, CLAUDE B., Editor. *California agriculture.* Univ. Calif. Press, Berkeley.

JOSEPHY, A. M., JR., Editor. 1961. *The American Heritage Book of Indians.* American Heritage, New York.

KROEBER, A. L. 1953. *Cultural and natural areas of native North America.* Univ. Calif. Press, Berkeley.

KROEBER, THEODORA. 1961. *Ishi in two worlds.* Univ. Calif. Press, Berkeley.

LEOPOLD, ALDO. 1949. *A sand county almanac.* Oxford Univ. Press, New York.

LEWIS, OSCAR. 1962. *This was San Francisco.* David McKay, New York.

MALONEY, A. B. 1945. *John Work, 1832–1833.* Fur brigade to the Bonaventura. Calif. Histo. Soc. Publ., San Francisco.

MATTHES, FRANÇOIS E. 1950. *The incomparable valley.* Univ. Calif. Press, Berkeley.

MCARDLE, RICHARD E. 1955. *Timber resources for America's future.* United States Forest Service, Washington.

MCWILLIAMS, CAREY. 1949. *California: the great exception.* A. A. Wyn, New York.

MUIR, JOHN. 1913. *The mountains of California.* Century, New York.

MUMFORD, LEWIS. 1961. *The city in history*. Harcourt, Brace, and World, New York.

NADEAU, REMI. 1950. *The water seekers*. Doubleday, New York.

———. 1960. *Los Angeles from mission to modern city*. Longmans, Green, New York.

NATIONAL PARK SERVICE. 1964. *The redwoods*. U.S. Dept. of the Interior, Washington, D.C.

NORRIS, FRANK. 1901. *The octopus*. Doubleday, Page, New York.

PEARSALL, C. E., and others. 1943. *The quest for Qual-a-wa-loo*. Private printing. San Francisco.

PRIESTLEY, H. I. 1937. *A historical, political, and natural description of California by Pedro Fages, Soldier of Spain*. Univ. Calif. Press, Berkeley.

ROBINSON, W. W. 1948. *Land in California*. Univ. Calif. Press, Berkeley.

RUDD, ROBERT L. 1964. *Pesticides and the living landscape*. Univ. Wisc. Press, Madison.

SAUER, CARL. 1957. The end of the Ice Age and its witnesses. *Geographical Review*, 47: 29–43.

STAMP, L. DUDLEY. 1960. *Applied geography*. Penguin Books, Harmondsworth, England.

———, Editor. 1961. *A history of land use in arid regions*. UNESCO, Paris.

STEINBECK, JOHN. 1936. *In dubious battle*. Modern Library, New York.

———. 1939. *The grapes of wrath*. Viking Press, New York.

SUDWORTH, GEORGE B. 1908. *Forest trees of the Pacific slope*. U.S. Forest Service, Washington, D.C.

SULLIVAN, M. S. 1934. *The travels of Jedediah Smith*. Fine Arts Press, Santa Ana, Calif.

TEGGART, F. J. 1911. *The Portola expedition of 1769–1770. Diary of Miguel Costanso*. Univ. Calif. Publ., Academy of Pacific Coast History, 2: 4.

THOMAS, W. L., JR., Editor. 1956. *Man's role in changing the face of the earth*. Wenner-Gren and National Science foundations. Univ. Chicago Press, Chicago.

TURNER, WALLACE. 1963. Fight looms for California orchards. *New York Times,* Western Ed., Aug. 7.

UDALL, STEWART L. 1963. *The quiet crisis.* Holt, Rinehart and Winston, New York.

UNITED STATES BUREAU OF CENSUS. 1961. *Statistical abstract of the United States.* Gov't Printing Office, Washington, D.C.

UNITED STATES BUREAU OF RECLAMATION. 1950. *Central Valley Project, California.* Gov't Printing Office, Washington.

UNITED STATES DEPARTMENT OF AGRICULTURE. 1963. *A place to live.* Yearbook of Agriculture. Gov't Printing Office, Washington, D.C.

UNITED STATES FOREST SERVICE. 1936. *The western range.* Senate Document 199, Gov't Printing Office, Washington, D.C.
————. 1956. *Timber resources review.* Gov't Printing Office, Washington, D.C.

VAN DYKE, T. S. 1902. The deer and elk of the Pacific Coast. *The Deer Family* by Theodore Roosevelt and others. Macmillan, New York.

VAUX, HENRY J. 1955. *Timber in Humboldt county.* Bull. 748, Calif. Agric. Exp. Sta., Berkeley.

WENTWORTH, E. N. 1948. *America's sheep trails.* Iowa State College Press, Ames, Iowa.

WOHLETZ, L. R., and E. F. DOLDER. 1952. *Know California's land.* Calif. Dept. Natural Resources, Sacramento.

WOLFE, L. M. 1938. *John of the mountains; the unpublished journals of John Muir.* Houghton Mifflin, Boston.

WOOD, SAMUEL E., and A. E. HELLER. 1962. California Going, Going . . . California tomorrow, Sacramento.

ZEUNER, FREDERICK E. 1950. *Dating the past: an introduction to geochronology.* Methuen, London.

Index